DREDGING FOR GOLD . . .

THE GOLD DIVERS' HANDBOOK

AN ILLUSTRATED GUIDE TO THE HOBBY OF UNDERWATER GOLD PROSPECTING

by Matt Thornton

FRONT COVER: "A Dredger Does His Thing,"
photo by Matt Thornton

BACK COVER: "A Nugget Is Found," series of photos courtesy
of Jerry Keene

All photographs and illustrations throughout the book are by the
Author, except where otherwise noted. Matt Thornton's
original graphic concepts for the line drawings and hand
sketches were redrawn by George M. Stroud.

Third Printing, April 1979

Library of Congress Catalog Card Number: 75-7745

PRINTED AND BOUND IN THE UNITED STATES OF AMERICA

PUBLISHED BY KEENE INDUSTRIES
9330 CORBIN AVENUE
NORTHRIDGE, CALIFORNIA 91324
(213) 993-0411

TABLE OF CONTENTS

PREFACE

The hobby of recreational gold prospecting is one that has grown by leaps and bounds within the past ten years or so, and just about every aspect of gold prospecting has one or more authoritative "guidebooks" to aid the person who is just getting started in that particular activity. There are countless books on the subjects of gold panning, sluicing, metal detecting . . . well, you *name* a particular phase of prospecting and somebody's written a book about it. But in the midst of this massive collection of literature, there is one aspect of gold prospecting for which there *is no* guidebook to follow — until now, that is. This is the subject of gold-dredging. Oh, sure, there have been a couple of books on gold-dredging in the past, but today these are virtually obsolete in light of recent advances that have been made in the technology of underwater gold mining. What the prospecting world *needs* is a good, factual, up-to-date, no-nonsense book on the technically involved subject of underwater gold-dredging, and that's what inspired me to write this book — "Dredging for Gold . . . The Gold Divers' Handbook."

The sport of recreational gold-dredging has grown phenomenally in recent years, and the sale of dredging equipment and related accessories has mushroomed into a multimillion-dollar-a-year business. In years past, when fewer persons were engaged in gold-dredging, newcomers learned the ins and outs of the hobby by actually *doing it.* Many gold-dredgers of past years were actual citizens of the gold country and tended to "fall into" underwater mining the same way a bird takes to flying, but today it is the "flatlander" who dominates the dredging scene. He's the person who works five days a week in the depressing atmosphere of the big city, looking forward to weekends when he can journey to God's Country and play "'49er" for a while. I must be perfectly honest by stating that I, myself, am also a "flatlander"; only *this* flatlander has "paid his dues" and knows what the whole thing is about.

I have written this book primarily for the person who knows absolutely *nothing* about gold-dredging, aside from the fact that he or she wants to get started in it. As you progress through the Chapters of this book, you will learn the subject of gold-dredging *in steps,* starting out with basic, introductory information, working up to the anatomy of a gold dredge, how to research an area for gold potential, how to select a precise location for dredging, how to sample a stream, what equipment is needed for underwater diving, and finally culminating in Chapter Eleven which puts all the previous information together for the purpose of describing the various methods of conducting an actual dredging operation.

I have included a number of Chapters on "specialty" areas of the prospecting field, which will be of help to the dredger once he gets more deeply involved in the sport. For example, I have taken what I believe to be a "giant step for 'dredgerkind' " by including a Chapter that deals exclusively with the legal aspects of mining. The complex subjects of mining law and claim filing are explained here in language that is easily understood by the reader, things which I have never seen in earlier books on gold-dredging.

The subject of gold amalgamation has been touched upon in just about every book ever written on the hobby of recreational gold prospecting, but not in the kind of detail that is so tremendously important in light of the complex subject matter. Well, that's what Chapter Twelve is about — *gold amalgamation.* In offering information as detailed as that to be found in this Chapter, I am not implying that amalgamation is a technique to be used for curing every case of the "fine gold recovery blues." Rather, it is a technique that should be used only if you *really need to use it.* Chapter Twelve should help you arrive at a decision in this matter.

Chapter Thirteen is devoted entirely to the fine art of prospecting for gold with a metal detector. This is a very fascinating subject on which a lot has been written in years past; unfortunately, much of the previously published information isn't worth a hill of beans in light of today's extremely sophisticated "VLF" metal detector technology. Even though metal detectors have no use in actual underwater dredging operations, "nugget-shooting" is a great activity for those occasional days when a gold-dredger wakes up in the morning, eats breakfast, and doesn't quite feel like getting into his wet suit. What does a diver do in a case like this? He reaches for his metal detector, that's what!

The book you now hold in your hands represents the third printing of "Dredging for Gold . . . The Gold Divers' Handbook." After making a detailed inspection of the second printing (which came out in May of 1977), I found a number of things which required updating in order to keep pace with changing times. Something new I have included in "Dredging for Gold . . ." is a piece of highly important new information concerning the way placer gold is deposited in many river systems. I call this new information my "Sequence of Tailings Principle," and this is the very first time it has appeared in any book on gold prospecting. If you'll take the time to really study it thoroughly, it just might increase your gold recovery by ten thousand per cent. You'll find this new information at the end of Chapter Seven.

Matthew R. (Matt) Thornton

March, 1979
Hollywood, California

ACKNOWLEDGEMENTS

On the acknowledgements page of any book, it is customary to list the names of all persons who have aided you in the process of transforming your manuscript into a finished product. In my case, I can think of three people really worthy of mention.

First, I must thank the good people at Keene Industries of Northridge, California, for providing me the photographs of gold-dredging equipment that are shown in Chapter Four of this book. The color photographs on the back cover are also courtesy of Keene Industries, and I am indebted to Jerry Keene for having provided them to me.

Putting together a book of this magnitude is no small task, and one person who really went above and beyond the call of duty is Merlin "Whitey" Becktold. Whitey is the man responsible for expediting the setting of type and the shooting of all photographs, veloxes and line negatives — in other words, everything one needs in order to lay out and "paste up" a book! Without Whitey and his fellow workers at United Western Enterprises of Santa Monica, California, the job of putting together "Dredging for Gold . . . The Gold Divers' Handbook" would have been much more difficult.

Finally, a huge round of applause is due for my close friend (and fellow gold-dredger), Dick Arthurs, who braved the frigid temperature of a December day to pose for the photograph on the front cover of this book. (The icebergs were floating just out of camera range!) Dick also posed for the nugget-shooting pictures in Chapter Thirteen, and again, I owe him my thanks.

"Respectfully dedicated to Dick, Jerry, Gordon, Bill, Steve, Bob, Don and Virginia, all of whom had a profound effect on my early days as a gold miner; without them, this book would not have been possible."

CHAPTER ONE
The Nature of the Stuff Called "Gold"

Of all the cherished and sought-after substances placed by God upon this planet earth, none is revered as much as a certain heavy, yellow metal that goes by the name GOLD. For the past six thousand years (give or take a few centuries), men have schemed for it, murdered each other for it, fought wars over it, and, on a less violent tone, enticed the most beautiful women in history for it . . . all for that fascinating, yellow substance known simply as "gold."

What is the underlying cause of such a great love affair, one that seemingly afflicts each and every human being on this planet? Put this question to the top scientific minds of our day and even they can't tell you; what they *can* tell you is that gold is one of the ninety-two naturally-occurring elements that make up this celestial spaceship we are all traveling on. If you push a little harder, they'll reveal that gold is the seventy-ninth member of this large family, that it is a heavy, extremely dense metal of great malleability and ductility (more on that later), and that it goes by the chemical symbol "AU." They'll go on to say that gold has been used as the basis of the world's monetary systems for well over two thousand years, yet they can't tell you *why* gold was chosen to play such an important role in the affairs of men and nations. To understand the ever-intriguing nature of gold, we will need to do a little detective work on our own; quite a few assumptions will have to be made along the way.

Gold may well have been the first metal prehistoric man became acquainted with. This is understandable, because gold in its familiar "nugget" form (the type commonly found in stream beds) is perhaps the most striking and noticeable substance occurring in nature. An ancient cave-dweller whose name has been lost to history probably caught the first glint of gold in the form of a few small nuggets along the rocky bed of a dry river and, picking them up to examine them more closely, was impressed by the "heft" of the little pieces of metal. The more our long-deceased friend examined the substance, the glowing, yellow color that so distinguishes gold from other metals began to play strange tricks on his mind. It is possible that ancient man associated the yellow color of gold with the friendly and comforting warmth of the sun, a theory that is greatly substantiated if you advance thousands of years in time to examine the Inca Empire of South America. In that civilization, gold *was* associated with the sun, and in no small way. The worship of the sun god was one of the prime aspects of Inca life, and this "gold-sun" relationship was by no means confined to the Incas. On our own North American continent, gold was both respected and feared by the various Indian tribes of the West. It was respected for its great lustre and beauty, and feared for its ability to lure the white man into territory that had been held sacred for countless generations. Perhaps the Apaches phrased it best — to them, nuggets of gold were "tears wept by the sun."

As ancient man moved out of the dark, turbulent era known as the "stone age" and into the light of day (approximately 6,000 to 8,-000 B.C., depending upon which archaeologist you believe), many changes took place. Man lay aside his weapons of the hunt and began settling into small, but permanent communities. Farming and animal-husbandry became the important occupations of the day, and it wasn't long before one community began encountering other communities. As man became acquainted with his neighbors, he undoubtedly noticed that his newly found friends had goods and materials that he didn't have. He also noticed that there were many things, both tangible and intangible, that were common to both communities. It is highly probable that gold was one such commodity.

Hundreds, and eventually, thousands of years passed. The world had seen such wonders as Mesopotamia, the splendor of Egypt, and the Golden Age of Greece. Ancient man had, by this time, sailed over great bodies of water and encountered civilizations newer and stranger than anything he had yet seen. But wherever he went in his outward quest for knowledge and adventure, he found one thing to be the same for *all* civilizations, *all* men — that was the love of gold.

In the sixth century B.C., the rich and powerful King Croesus of the Lydian Empire took an important step — he issued an oblong piece of gold from his mint (which, incidentally, produced the world's first coinage) and gave it the name *money.* Such a move was completely logical in that since gold was loved and cherished in all the then-existing countries, why not use it as a universal medium of exchange for goods and services? After all, wasn't gold the only substance that could be handled time and time again without losing its shape, without rusting or corroding, or without spoiling or rotting? Wasn't it the only substance that could be exposed (though certainly not intentionally) to the harsh effects of wind and weather and come through unscathed? Wasn't it the only substance that could withstand flood, earthquake, fire and still display that brilliantly characteristic sheen? Of course it was, and those are the reasons for gold being what it is today — *now* — in the twentieth century A.D. It is true, unfortunately, that gold's role as the unit of monetary exchange is being played down, but today gold is performing *new* roles that hold promise of a very exciting future for a heavy yellow metal that up until the early 1960's was considered good for nothing more than coinage, jewelry, and dental work. To use a current expression, "It's a new day, baby, and the times they are a-changin'!"

Few people realize it, but the same gold they once loved and cherished for nothing more than warmth, color, and security has now been classified as one of today's "space-age" metals. How, do you ask, does gold find a place in the incredibly complex technology of the 1970's? To start out, everyone (or at least I *think* everyone) has heard of the electronics industry. They're the ones that manufacture radios, televisions, cassette players, mini-calculators, that sort of thing. Without gold, the precision circuit boards and microelectronic components of these products would not be as reliable as they are. Gold is a very good conductor of electricity, and is used in the fine "lines" of printed metal that carry current from one component to the other. If this doesn't impress you, let's jump over to the aerospace industry, including the very specialized department that occasionally sends man into orbit. Again, it is not surprising to find gold being used in electronic circuitry, this time in extremely sophisticated on-board computer systems of space capsules. Wherever the utmost in reliability is required, you will find gold.

Few people realize it, but gold is one of the best radiation shields there is; the space program makes wide use of gold when it comes to protecting astronauts from the harsh environment of space. A good example of this would be the plastic faceshield of an astronaut's spacesuit. Gold is a most remarkable metal. One of its many properties is *malleability,* meaning it can be pounded or compressed into various shapes and thicknesses without breaking or returning to its original form. Gold is the most malleable of all metals, and can be pounded down so fantastically thin you can actually see light through it. When such a layer of gold is imbedded in an astronaut's faceshield, the individual inside can see out, whereas heat, glare, and deadly radiation cannot come in. This same principle is now being applied to windows for earthbound homes and commercial buildings.

Another of gold's noteworthy properties is *ductility,* the ability to be stretched or drawn without breaking. Gold is remarkably ductile, and can be drawn out into a wire so fine it is practically invisible; it has been estimated that a mere *ounce* of gold could be drawn into a wire fifty miles long! Naturally, such a wire would be far too fine for all but the most sub-miniature of applications, yet industry, electronics, and jewelers do use much gold wire of thicker gauge; some of this "thicker" wire is pretty thin in its own right.

Chemically, gold is very inert — this means it does not readily form compounds with other elements found in nature. Gold is classified as a "Noble" metal, meaning no substance that occurs commonly in nature can destroy it. There are exceptions, of course. A blend of nitric and hydrochloric acids, known as "aqua regia," will dissolve the yellow stuff. Gold can be corroded somewhat by bombarding it with pure chlorine gas, but how often does pure chlorine gas occur in nature? Gold can also (and *is,* in gold extraction mills) be dissolved by a solution of sodium cyanide. Of course, even though the gold is dissolved in the solution, it can always be recovered by bringing the solution into contact with powdered zinc, which has an even greater affinity for gold than the cyanide. The zinc-gold compound that results from this "marriage" is placed in a special furnace, fired up to a temperature of 2,400 degrees Fahrenheit, melted, and poured into molds. The gold will settle to the bottom, while the zinc floats to the surface as slag. What all this amounts to is this — even though gold can seemingly be "destroyed" by man-made chemical compounds, it can always be restored to its ever-beautiful, solid, hefty, substantial yellow form.

It is no small wonder, then, that gold is highly sought-after today, just as in the days of the great gold rushes of the past century. The *equipment* used nowadays for recovering gold may be a great deal different than anything the Forty-Niners used, but the disease known as "gold fever" is as prevalent as ever. Today, it is the recreational miner who reigns supreme, the man who likes to get away from the crushing, depressing atmosphere of the big city and out into the fresh air and sunshine. He does not place great importance on "striking it rich," though the possibility is definitely there (more on that in Chapter Three). He is a man who likes to do things somewhat out of the ordinary, a man who pursues a challenging hobby activity. Gold prospecting is all of these things, and more.

There are many methods of searching for gold in the 1970's. You can use the ever-popular gold pan, coupled with pick and shovel, and try your luck in a neighboring stream. One of the many fine electronic metal detectors manufactured today can also be taken along on such a trip to engage in a popular sport known as "nugget-shooting." On an entirely different note, you can purchase a machine known as a "dry-washer" (or sometimes *electrostatic concentrator*) and prospect the many dry gulches in our Southwestern desert areas. Or, you can purchase an even *more* sophisticated piece of equipment known as a "suction dredge," and participate in what has proven to be one of the fastest-growing hobbies today — *underwater prospecting.*

The many thousands of participants in the "sport" of underwater prospecting (more commonly known as *gold-dredging*) have the distinction of producing more gold, ounce for ounce, than all other types of recreational gold mining combined. There are several reasons for this. First, a gold-dredger actually goes down *beneath* the surface of a river or stream and removes gravel from the bottom, thereby uncovering cracks and fissures in the bedrock which hold gold the original argonauts couldn't touch. Second, because of the nature of streamflow characteristics, many deposits of gold are replenished year after year; if you recovered ten or twenty ounces of gold from a rich gravel bar, you could very possibly return to that same bar a few years later and remove ten or twenty *more*. This type of large-scale replenishment occurs in streams which drain vast areas of gold-laden "hydraulic" mine tailings. The gold contained in the tailings is flushed into the rivers during periodic winter "killer floods," to eventually settle in the same areas previously "cleaned out" by dredgers.) Third, and perhaps the most important, is the fact that there are many prospectors who wouldn't even *think* of going underwater in their quest for gold, being more than content to pan material from the banks and go home with a few flakes. This only makes things better for those who *do* dive.

When a person considers all these factors, one thing immediately comes to mind — there are many hundreds of miles of river bottom in the United States that have *never been worked* for the values they contain, values that can be quite substantial at times. It is this indisputable fact that makes gold-dredging such an exciting proposition.

CHAPTER TWO
The History of Dredging for Gold

Persons today who become interested in gold-dredging may tend to think of it as a new hobby activity born within the past few years, but actually, the underwater mining of gold is as old as the great California Gold Rush of the past century. Many historical accounts of this exciting period in history may lead the reader to believe that the original '49ers were ignorant of the immense gold deposits to be found at the bottoms of the various mountain streams; in reality, nothing could be further from the truth. The argonauts of the late 1840's and 50's were *very much* aware of these rich gold deposits, but the majority of them didn't worry about gold that, for all practical purposes, may as well have been on the surface of the moon. There were a number of determined miners who attempted to recover gold from the depths of some of the richer gold-bearing rivers, but information on these early operations is scant. We do know that the majority of "first generation" gold-divers were of Chinese or Hawaiian extraction, and quite possibly a number of divers came to the Western gold country from South American provinces such as Colombia, where gold-bearing rivers had already been mined for centuries.

The site of James Marshall's gold discovery at Coloma, on the South Fork of the American River, probably was the site of the earliest known gold-diving operation in this country. In the year 1849, just one year after Marshall's electrifying discovery, brave divers equipped with nothing more than crude hand tools attempted to recover gold from the South Fork of the American River at this extremely rich location, just a stone's throw from John A. Sutter's sawmill. Early diving operations such as these were often fatal to the man who ventured underwater, as he was often caught off guard by vicious currents that are so characteristic of mountain streams.

In spite of the dangers, gold-diving on a small scale spread to other mining districts and continued on into the 1880's, when the first machines worthy of the name "suction dredge" were invented. These early gold dredges were operated by steam engines, and were employed principally in California's Feather, Yuba and Stanislaus River systems. The divers who worked with these rigs could probably command the distinction of being the first true gold-dredgers, as they worked on the bottoms of the streams loosening hard-packed gravels as well as trying to prevent larger rocks from clogging the dredge's intake.

The turn of the century saw new techniques evolving in the field of underwater gold mining. Some of the steam-powered dredges mentioned in the previous paragraph were augmented with caissons extending down to the bottom of the river, allowing the diver below to work with improved efficiency. As was the case with most types of gold mining equipment, caisson dredges made their first appearance in California.

The forerunner of today's deep-sea diving dress was employed in various gold-bearing streams during the early 1900's, and for the first time, the underwater miner was able to work in chilling waters for lengthy periods. Older publications on gold mining frequently refer to these suits as "sub-aqueous armour." Though such equipment was quite primitive by today's diving standards, it would be hard to distinguish an early gold-diver wearing such a suit from a deep-sea diver of the 1970's. Diving for gold in sub-aqueous armour became quite popular during the early decades of the 1900's, but there were hazards. Many an early gold-diver went to a watery grave due to the extremely crude, hand-operated air pumps in use at the time. These pumps had a tendency to go haywire at inopportune moments, causing the diver's death if he were working in deep water and unable to return to the surface in time. If he *did* make a sudden return to the surface from a substantial depth, even if he made it back up before passing out from lack of oxygen, chances are he would develop either one of two extremely dangerous conditions known today as "air embolism," or "the bends." (These conditions will be discussed in detail in Chapter Ten.)

The dark days of the great Depression of the 1930's saw a boom in all types of gold mining, especially in the major hardrock mines of the California Mother Lode country. Thousands of men were employed in famous mining centers such as Nevada City, Grass Valley, Jackson, Plymouth, Alleghany, and others too numerous to mention. But the great prosperity so prevalent in "them thar hills" was a complete, 180-degree turnabout from the rest of the country. Older readers of this book will recall with much despair the turbulent economic conditions of the period, when soup lines and songs such as "Buddy, Can You Spare Me a Dime?" were the order of the day. With such a vast amount of people out of work, with nothing to look forward to, the interest in gold among the man on the street skyrocketed. The ordinary man out of work could not in any way take on the sort of operation used by the giant underground mines, so he took the easiest way out — he went to the rivers, as did his ancestors back in 1849.

The Gold Rush of the 1930's may not have been anything like that of 1849, but the amount of people engaged in river mining during the days of the Depression was considerable, especially in California where streams were (and still are, for that matter) constantly being replenished with new gold washed down from the mountains of old hydraulic mine tailings lining the banks. These tailings themselves contained only a few cents worth of gold per cubic yard, but remarkable things happened since the year 1884 when hydraulic mining was banned. Intervening years of heavy, winter rains washed the tailings down into the streams, and the gold contained in the waste material was re-concentrated into pockets not unlike those originally discovered by the '49ers during the first Gold Rush. These new deposits, of course, were not as rich as those worked by the original argonauts, but they did nevertheless reveal themselves to those with the time and patience to search for them. With thousands of persons unemployed during the 1930's, there were *all sorts* of people to search for them, and search they did.

The vast majority of gold-seekers during the Depression utilized the "basic four" prospecting tools — pick, shovel, bucket, and sluice box. It was relatively simple for the inexperienced miner to locate banks of gravel along the edges of a river that contained fair amounts of gold, and once such a deposit was located the gravel was shoveled into the buckets, carried down to the river and washed through the sluice box. Thousands of persons in the Western mining states were able to take two or three dollars a day in gold, which was a goodly sum of money back then. The ones who found *more* than this didn't dare breathe a word of it!

During my travels in the gold country, I've run into old prospectors who have told me of suction dredging operations during the 1930's that utilized gasoline-powered dredges with engines taken from Model A passenger cars! I have researched these stories further by talking with knowledgeable mining men, and they say they've *never* heard of such dredges. Now I'm not saying it's impossible for an ingenious individual to have built himself a suction dredge using a "Model A-powered water vacuum system," as the knowledge and technology were definitely there. It is simply the lack of concrete evidence that makes this author a skeptic concerning suction dredging during the 1930's.

Underwater gold mining saw its first great innovation during the late 1940's, following the introduction of Self-Contained Underwater Breathing Apparatus, known the world over as SCUBA. For the first time, the underwater prospector was freed of the "life line" that connected him with the world topside. The gold-diver could now strap a couple of compressed air tanks on his back, dive into the river, and mine to his heart's content for one or two hours at a time. If he saw a likely-looking spot ten or twenty feet away from where he entered the stream, he could move there and sample it without worrying about running out of life line. (SCUBA equipment is employed by gold-divers today, but has been pushed into the background by the simpler and more practical "Hookah" system. This will be discussed in detail in Chapter Ten.)

Gold-*diving* may have taken that "one giant step" in the late 40's, but it was really during the 1950's when the equipment for actual gold-*dredging* came into wide popular use. Before the 50's, dredging equipment was scarce, and dredges were constructed mainly by the individuals who were going to be using them; there were no establishments in the business of mass-producing underwater dredging gear for the general public. In the late 50's, this situation changed when a large number of one-man shops (often operating out of an individual's garage) sprang into existence. The majority of these shops were located in California, and turned out a mere handful of dredging units before quietly going out of business.

Gold-dredging in the late 50's and early 1960's was something of an adventure, because you didn't know exactly *what* you might find. Actually, I should use the words "how much," as that's what it amounted to. It was not uncommon for dredgers of this era to take fantastic amounts of gold from rivers which, in many instances, were finally freeing their channels of the tons of silt which had been deposited by numerous hydraulic mines of the old days. Dredgers who got there *first*, soon after the rivers got down to their normal channels, had a field day, because they were able to work crevices in the bedrock which had laid completely undisturbed since the time when their channels were first cluttered with hydraulic debris. In many cases, such crevices had been accidentally bypassed by the original Argonauts of a century ago, and had probably been collecting their golden treasure over a period of several thousand years.

Gold-dredging in the late 50's and early sixties was largely centered on the North Yuba River in California's Sierra County. It was on this river that the forerunners of today's gold dredges were first tested. There was also one heck of a lot of gold dredged from this river during this period, and perhaps the most famous gold-dredger on the North Fork was a gentleman by the name of Ernest Keene. Mr. Keene perhaps had the distinction of being the *gold-dredgers'* gold-dredger, and to this day underwater prospectors still talk of this gentleman's exploits on the North Yuba. Using equipment he designed and built himself, Ernie Keene recovered many hundreds, and often thousands of dollars worth of gold per day (at the old $35-an-ounce price, mind you) from deep river holes that had never been touched by the original '49ers. No other gold-dredger of the time wanted anything to do with Ernie Keene's "gold holes," which often reached frightening depths of sixty, seventy, or sometimes even eighty feet. (By comparison, most recreational gold-diving today is done in less than *ten* feet of water!) Unlike many of the original argonauts of 1849, Ernie Keene didn't squander his gold at the nearest Fandango hall; instead, he used it to start a company which, since 1958, has grown into one of the largest manufacturers of suction dredging equipment. This company bears his name, *Keene Industries.* Ironically, Mr. Keene was not destined to see gold-dredging, or his company, reach their respective zeniths. He passed away in 1961 following an airplane mishap.

Gold-dredging today rarely takes on the proportions of an Ernest Keene type of operation, but is more likely to consist of an active family going out together on a weekend and participating in something a little bit out of the ordinary. The dredging equipment of yesteryear was heavy, cumbersome, and required a goodly amount of strength to operate it, but today the underwater prospector can engage in his hobby using a complete "mini-dredge" that weighs a mere thirty-four pounds! There are, of course, larger dredges available for persons wishing to move and process entire gravel bars, but even these rigs weigh considerably less than equipment manufactured a mere ten years ago. What it all boils down to is this — gold-dredging, coupled with modern gold-dredging equipment, has reached the "state of the art," and now is as good a time as any to "take the plunge" and delve into this fascinating, clean, healthy, invigorating outdoor activity. Don't let misinformed persons convince you that the "'49ers took out all the gold back during the Gold Rush." There is plenty of gold remaining to be found — *today* — and if you want solid, concrete proof . . . well, Chapter Three of our study is just around the corner.

CHAPTER THREE

Is There *Really* Gold to be Found?

Whenever people learn of my involvement with underwater gold prospecting, they are certain to ask questions such as, "Do you really find gold? Have you ever found enough to make you rich? What's the most gold you ever found at one time?" I always give the same answers — *yes, no,* and *that's my business,* in that order. I try to tell people I dredge gold mainly as a form of recreation, and that I think of it as a get-rich-quick scheme only as a last resort. I personally have never faced a financial situation desperate enough to warrant my going out and dredging gold for a living, but nevertheless, people will always ask questions about this particular side of the coin. Perhaps people have a deep-down belief that the '49ers *did* remove all the gold from the rivers back during the Gold Rush, and they make these inquiries either to have their theories substantiated or else dashed to bits on the nugget-studded bedrock of a swift mountain stream. Others merely wish to hear fantastic success stories — say, for example, of how "a couple of needy college kids bought a dredge, set it up in the nearest local creek, and recovered ten thousand dollars in gold over a long three-day weekend." Now, you should realize that yarns similar to the foregoing are a dime a dozen — but if it's confirmation of the existence of gold in today's rivers you seek, read further. I'm going to tell you some of the most incredible stories about gold and gold-dredging you've ever read. What's incredible about them is the fact that each and every one of *these* stories is true!

One basic question commonly thrown at me is, "Do I have to pack my dredge way into the back country in order to make a killing?" Up until the summer of 1971, I used to give a firm "yes" to this query, until a couple of divers uncovered one of the more significant dredging finds of the past few years. I won't mention the names of these lucky gold-divers as they would be hunted down and hounded unmercifully, but I will tell their story.

In the summer of '71, the aforementioned divers were dredging a "hole" in the Middle Fork of the Yuba River, one of the richer gold-bearing streams in northern California. (In the vernacular of underwater prospecting, a "hole" is usually a deep, natural pool in a major river or stream where the current slows and deposits the heavier materials it has been carrying in suspension.) The hole in question is less than five hundred feet downstream from a major county road crossing and camping site that usually sees a dozen or more persons on any summer weekend. Our two anonymous divers had sampled this area several times, and in 1971 they finally decided to dredge the spot. Using a custom "super dredge" with a high-powered Peugeot engine, the divers proceeded to work their way down through the "overburden," the dredgers' term for the generally worthless gravel that covers the bedrock of a stream. In this case the overburden was thicker than usual, over twenty feet in fact! Upon reaching the ultimate depth of twenty-eight feet, our divers hit a bonanza beyond their wildest dreams, and in the ensuing days and weeks removed over 200 ounces of coarse, nugget-sized gold from the bedrock. One crevice alone on the bottom of the stream yielded *five pounds* of gold! What makes me somewhat ill is the fact that I had stood near this very location several months prior to this remarkable discovery thinking to myself, "No, there can't be anything here." I suppose I thought wrong!

Wolf Creek in Sierra County, California, is a tributary of the Middle Fork of the Yuba River, the same Middle Yuba mentioned in the previous story. It, too, is one of the richer gold streams of northern California, and is associated with a number of rich gold finds in the past few years. We shall study one of Wolf Creek's more noteworthy outlays.

Again, let's return to the summer of 1971, around the same time our first pair of intrepid divers was striking it rich in the Middle Yuba. This story also concerns two individuals, and they, too, will remain anonymous for reasons obvious. These two gentlemen located an area on Wolf Creek where the banks had been mined by hydraulic methods during the late 1800's. In this particular mining operation, the gravel was washed down onto a series of long wooden boards to be routed to a sluice box located some distance downstream. Over the months and years the operation was conducted, the spaces between the boards gradually enlarged and pieces of gold fell through the separations and onto the ground underneath. A few measly pieces of gold lost in such a manner didn't bother the original miners, as they were only after the "big stuff." In time the deposit played out and the hydraulickers moved on to better diggings, leaving Wolf Creek to flow peacefully into the twentieth century.

The two men in question had been searching the edges of Wolf Creek for promising dredging spots when, by chance, they happened to dig into a gravel bar located fifteen or twenty feet away from the stream. The bar yielded gold, and in generous amounts. Whether they realized it at the time or not, they had stumbled onto the patch of ground that had laid underneath the wooden boarding used to direct the hydraulic gravels to the sluice box! It didn't take our friends long to set up a plan of operation — they would dig a large hole at the site by hand, use the pump on their gold dredge to fill the hole with water, and then *dredge the gravel out of the hole.* Their idea must have worked, for they recovered 137 ounces of some of the prettiest gold ever seen!

As we have observed thus far, 1971 was a banner year for rich dredging discoveries. By now I know you must be sick of reading about 1971, but before we move on to other summers I'd like to tell you about one other major find made in the summer of that year; this one *still* has me up in the air!

In the spring of 1972, a young man came into a local prospecting shop where I hang out, looking much like a person who might be contemplating the purchase of his first piece of mining equipment. What struck me funny, though, was the fact that he was literally covered with gold nuggets — on his rings, his belt buckle, his tie bar — *everywhere.* After I pressed the matter slightly, he revealed that he had been dredging in California's North Fork of the American River for virtually all of 1971. It seems he had been laid off from his job with the aerospace industry, which at that time was very much in trouble. (Thousands of persons in California were laid off in '70 and '71, and now I realize that at least *one* of them tried his hand at gold-dredging.)

This young man made his appearance on the North Fork in January of '71, not a very good time to be mining underwater. Rivers in California run high, fast, and extremely muddy at this time of year, but the man in question was not bothered by these factors. He was using a medium-sized dredge to poke sample holes into a large gravel bar known as "Big Bend," namely because that's what the North Fork does at this location — it makes a *big bend.* All throughout January, February, March, April and May he continued his sampling, finding a few ounces of gold here and there for his laborious efforts. If you've never visited this area on the North Fork, let me tell you about it. Big Bend is, indeed, a fitting name for this stretch of river, but the gravel bar right at the tip of the bend where this man was dredging should more fittingly be named "Boulder Beach." This man, using nothing more than a simple hand winch, winched aside rocks so large a man would be crushed instantly if one of them ever fell over on him. But back to our story. . . .

On June 10, 1971, things started happening when our young friend hit the bottom of the river and found it to be covered with a layer of incredibly hard, cemented blue clay, known to the gold-diving crowd as "hardpack." It took him two full days to chisel *(literally)* through the hardpack, but when he finally got through and hit the actual bedrock . . . OH, BOY! He was rewarded for his months of work by long crevices in the bedrock, *filled with nuggets.* Some days he would recover six ounces, the next day five, perhaps seven ounces the next day. He continued mining until October, when he finally gave in and called it quits. As he told me later, "When it got to the point where I was only making an ounce a day, I said to hell with it." What was the total take come quitting time in October? Hold onto your hats, because it totaled up to a whopping 384 ounces of gold!

California is not the only Western state that's rich in gold — our next story takes place in southern Oregon, in the beautiful Illinois River country to be exact.

Those of us associated with mining have the pleasure of meeting all sorts of interesting people, and not too long ago I met an aircraft pilot at the aforementioned prospecting shop. We got to talking about flying in general, and I expressed my desire of owning a plane so that I could fly mining equipment into my favorite dredging spots. The pilot then related one of his own interesting experiences which took place several years ago while flying a party into the wilderness of southern Oregon. This party consisted of several prospectors who were searching for likely dredging spots.

One day, the pilot had set his plane down in a clearing near the Illinois River, and the entire group set out to explore the area. After scouting for a few hours, they came upon an old cabin close to the river. The men hollered out to see if anyone was around, but there was no reply. The pilot then walked up to the cabin and looked into one of its open windows. There, on the mantle over the crude fireplace, were several mayonnaise jars filled to the brim with large gold nuggets! The pilot stared at this treasure for several moments, trying to convince himself he was not dreaming. He thought about going into the cabin to look at the gold more closely, but he had reservations. It's a good thing he did, for when he finally turned around to walk away, the owner of the cabin was standing there with a shotgun pointed at his head! After a series of hasty explanations the landowner backed down and opened up to the prospecting party. "Yes," he said, "I'm working a rich spot. You probably saw my gold on the mantle." The group of prospectors asked the gentleman if they could dredge on his river frontage, but the man answered with a very definite "No." He did, however, direct the party to a nearby area and said, "Pan here." The men did, and every single pan of material taken from the surface of the ground yielded a fantastic showing of color.

The Illinois River and its many small tributaries are famous for rich pockets of gold, and it is very possible that other rich gold deposits are awaiting discovery. It is certain that many of them will be on land that is *open!*

Every so often someone will ask me, "What was the largest amount of gold that anyone ever found with a dredge?" This is an extremely difficult question to answer, as there have been a great number of noteworthy finds since suction dredging became widespread in the mid-1950's. A lot of the stories about rich dredging finds have to be taken with a grain of salt, as mining men (particularly *old-time* mining men) often have a tendency to exaggerate the facts. This is the case with the last of our "success stories," and you can take it any way you wish.

If you ever find yourself "paying your dues" at Big Bend on the North Fork of the American River (the same Big Bend mentioned in an earlier story), there is a good chance you will run into a middle-aged gentleman who resides in a house trailer parked near the large gravel bar at the tip of the bend. I won't mention this man's name for fear of possible waves of repercussion, but I will say he is something of a "legend" in the annals of California gold-dredging. If you ever strike up a conversation with this man, he will probably tell you about how he personally recovered *$120,000.00 in gold* from Big Bend during a six-week period in the summer of 1959.

Now let's take a moment to figure this out. At the time this remarkable (?) discovery supposedly took place, about the only outfit that was buying gold in such huge quantities was our own Uncle Sam (namely the United States Mint). The price of gold in 1959 was thirty-five dollars per Troy ounce, and was rigidly held at that level by the Federal Government. The price paid for raw gold, however, such as that taken from rivers, averaged about $31.50 per Troy ounce, which is ten per cent *less* than $35.00. (As will be explained later on in Chapter Six, most river gold consists of ninety per cent gold and ten per cent impurities such as silver — which the Government never paid you for — hence the $31.50 per ounce price.) If we do a little division to determine how many times $31.50 goes into $120,000.00, we come up with 3,809 and one-half ounces of gold which would, indeed, make this the largest dredging find of which there is any knowledge.

If the gentleman in question actually did make so incredible a find, you would never know it judging by his lifestyle of recent years. I last saw this man in October of 1969 as he operated a small tungsten claim near the old southern California mining town of Randsburg. He was living on the claim with his family in a crowded, dilapidated trailer that somehow failed to come up to the standards of "House Beautiful." It is true that ten years had elapsed since this man "struck it rich," yet you'd think there would be *something* left to indicate the substantial wealth he once supposedly had. There wasn't.

As a famous personality of the news media once said, "Time Marches On," and so is the case with our anonymous gentleman. He's back on the North Fork now, and you can often see him working the river in the general vicinity of Big Bend. You'd never know his story if you were to meet him under casual circumstances, but if you ever did get to know him, he would perhaps reward you by pulling out the one piece of evidence that can't really be explained away. This author has never actually seen it, but this man reportedly has in his possession a tattered, faded slip of paper that bears the trademark of the U.S. Government. It is a receipt from the United States Mint, made out to our anonymous gold-dredger, indicating a payment to him in the amount of $120,000.00. The rest I'll leave up to you.

The stories I have just related all concern large, significant finds made by gold-dredgers from 1959 (?) up until 1971. While these finds are indeed exciting, I feel it only fair to point out that such recoveries are relatively rare; such riches may be uncovered by only two or three dredgers each mining season. There are, however, *many hundreds* of underwater prospectors who annually recover ten, twenty, thirty ounces of gold or more from streams of the Western United States, and most of these people are just like you or I — they dredge gold as a means of *fun and recreation,* and push the importance of "striking it rich" into the background. The chances of making that one lucky find are there, to be sure, but if you get started in gold-dredging with the idea of recreation — not profit — firmly in mind, you will get a great deal more pleasure from this ever-fascinating *hobby* activity, which was the way it originated in the first place.

CHAPTER FOUR
A Beginners'
Guide to Gold Dredges

INTRODUCTION TO CHAPTER FOUR

In the three previous Chapters of this book we have discussed such subject areas as the historical nature of gold, the history of underwater gold-diving and dredging, and the existence of gold in rivers and streams in the twentieth century. We have progressed far enough along the line to the point where I can bring up the meatiest subject matter of all, that of the actual gold dredge itself.

This Chapter is divided into two sections, titled "the Anatomy of a Modern Gold Dredge" (Section A), and "How to Operate a Suction Dredge" (Section B).

In Section A we will discuss the operating theories of the different types of dredges, various methods of creating suction, selecting the right dredge for the right application, and more. In Section B you will find sound, basic operating hints to help you get the best possible performance from your gold dredge.

By breaking down the study material in this manner, you can get a better perspective of each aspect of the gold dredge, which will lead to a better overall understanding of the subject in the long run.

SECTION A
The Anatomy of a Modern Gold Dredge

Once upon a time, the words "gold dredge" were synonymous with a monstrously large, clanking, clattering piece of machinery that scooped up silt and gravel from the bottoms of rivers with huge steel buckets. These great machines first appeared in the late 1800's, reached their zenith during the Depression days of the 1930's, and have since faded away due to increased operating costs, a gold price which, until recently, was fixed, and environmental reasons.

I'm sure it's coincidental, but about the same time the last major "bucket dredges" were winding down operations (the late 1950's) the modern suction dredge arrived on the scene. To this day, mention the words "gold dredge" to the average person and he'll surely conjure up images of a large bucket rig. But a suction gold dredge has *no* steel buckets or anything of that nature — instead, it functions as an "underwater vacuum cleaner."

Suction gold dredges work on the *Venturi* hydromechanic principle to create the vacuum necessary for dredging. In the Venturi arrangement, water from the river is drawn into the intake of a free-flow, high-velocity centrifugal jetting pump, which in turn is powered by a portable gasoline engine. An engine of several horsepower is usually used, resulting in the discharge of a large gallonage of water from the pump output at an extremely high rate of speed. A length of hose capable of withstanding high pressure (known commonly as "pressure hose") is connected to the output of the pump, which carries the water flow from the pump to an *eduction device*.

There are three principal types of eduction devices for creating suction — suction nozzles, power-jets, and circle-jets. In all three types of eductors, the water coming from the pump is sent through a restricted opening known as an "orifice." When the flow of water emerging from the pump output is directed through a correctly designed orifice, pressure is created which induces a powerful suction action at the intake of the eduction device.

There are three principle types of suction dredges in common use today. These are *surface dredges, submersible dredges* (more commonly known as "underwater dredges"), and *sub-surface dredges*. Let's start out by discussing the surface dredge, as it is the most popular.

A surface suction dredge is a device that brings gravel, rocks, and water from the bottom of a river up to a sluice box mounted on the dredging unit itself. You've probably seen surface dredges in action many times. They're the rigs that have the engine, pump, and sluice box floating on inner tubes, plastic modules (or occasionally styrofoam pontoons), on the surface of a stream. Modern surface dredges use either a suction nozzle or power-jet eduction device to deliver the river gravel to the surface sluice box for separation and recovery.

The "suction nozzle" type of eductor has been employed on surface dredges since the early days. In this aspect of the Venturi principle, the water from the pump output goes down under the surface of the river via the pressure hose to a specially curved piece of steel tubing. In the middle of the curved portion is an orifice, and it is directed toward the back end of the curved tube. When the pump output goes through the orifice, a high-velocity jet stream is created which displaces the water inside the tube and causes a suction to commence at the front end. This is where gravel, rocks, and water are taken in. With the water acting as the carrying agent, the gravel and rocks will rush past the orifice and into a flexible plastic *suction hose* attached to the back of the suction nozzle. The suction hose carries the gravel and water up to the sluice box floating on the surface of the stream. (Figure 1)

At the sluice box, the material coming up from the bottom of the river is sent through a "baffle box." In most sluice boxes, the gravel mixture is shot up into the baffle box on a forty-five-degree angle, and when it hits the "face" of the baffle, it is forced into a circular pathway which creates a turbulent, "churning" action which breaks up any compacted material. The gravel then shoots down the back end of the baffle box to be forced over a perforated classifier screen which routes the gravel into the appropriate "current level" of the sluice.

When I use the term "current level," I speak of the speed at which the water flows at various levels in the main section of the sluice box where the riffles are located. In the upper level of the sluice box, the current will be much swifter than at the lower portion where the riffles are. This basic principle is used to the best advantage in a modern surface sluice, and the classifier screen is what makes it all happen.

When the gravel completes its circular travels through the baffle box, it is forced down onto the classifier screen which stands ap-

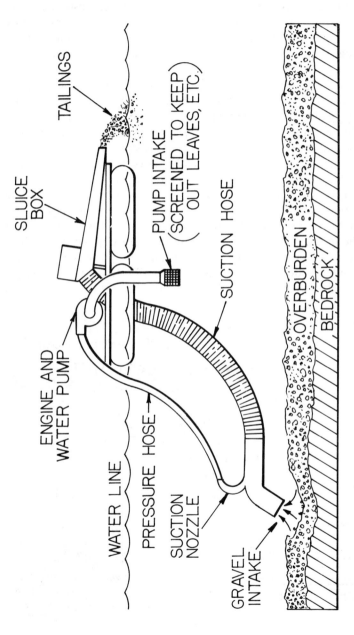

Figure 1—Suction nozzle type of surface dredge.

WATER LINE

PRESSURE HOSE

SUCTION NOZZLE

GRAVEL INTAKE

ENGINE AND WATER PUMP

SLUICE BOX

TAILINGS

PUMP INTAKE (SCREENED TO KEEP OUT LEAVES, ETC.)

SUCTION HOSE

OVERBURDEN

BEDROCK

33

proximately one inch off the floor of the sluice and covers the entire bottom portion of the baffle box. When the gravel hits the screen, two things happen — the gravel components which are *too large* to pass through the perforations of the screen (larger waste rocks) are deflected off into the fast current which flows through the upper level of the sluice. Once in the fast water, the waste rocks are carried through the sluice box to pour out of the discharge end with relatively little difficulty.

Gravel components that are *smaller* than the diameter of the classifier screen perforations usually will contain the most gold, and this type of gravel will be forced *through* the perforations and down to the bottom of the sluice where the current flows much slower. These gravels will "hug" the bottom of the sluice box and travel into the riffles at a gentler speed which better corresponds to their size. (Figure 2)

The most advanced (and also the most efficient) water-powered eduction device for use on a gold dredge is the power-jet. This device arrived on the gold-dredging scene during the late 1960's and in the intervening years has become the most popular of the three basic eduction devices. The theory behind the power-jet goes back a number of decades, and one "old-timer" told me it was actually patented way back in 1911. To be honest, I haven't tried to verify his

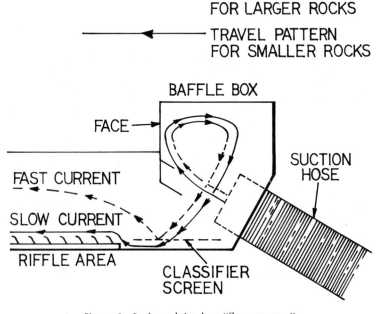

Figure 2—Surface sluice box "flow pattern."

statement, and therefore I can't necessarily go along with him.

The power-jet consists of an orifice assembly welded onto the side of a straight piece of metal tubing. In this arrangement, water from the pump output goes through the orifice as usual and then passes into the metal tube, one end of which is attached to the back of the surface sluice box. The other end is where the suction hose is attached, and this goes down to a plain intake "tip" at the bottom of the river. (Figure 3)

In operational theory, the only real difference between a power-jet and a suction nozzle is that the power-jet *pulls* the gravel and rocks up the suction hose from the surface; the suction nozzle *pushes* the gravel up to the surface from below. The surface sluice box functions in the same manner for both types of jets, only when using a power-jet there is a much stronger flow of water going through the sluice; this is true for the simple reason that the jet is located closer to the sluice box.

The basic power-jet, as stated earlier, has been widely used since the late '60s; however, in the past few years, some manufacturers have developed interesting variations on the original theme. Perhaps the most significant is known as a "four eductor," or "four banger" power-jet. Instead of utilizing a single orifice assembly welded onto the straight metal tube, the four eductor jet, as the name implies, has *four* orifice assemblies; these are spaced ninety degrees apart on the outside surface of the metal tubing, all of them the same distance from the end of the tube where the suction hose is coupled on. All four orifice assemblies are fed by a single "water manifold," which is a round, enclosed chamber encircling the straight metal tube, with openings into the four eductors. The pressure hose from the dredge's pump output is coupled to the water manifold. When the dredge engine is started and the manifold fills with water, four jet streams — all equal in velocity and pressure — shoot into the straight metal tube. This "quadradial" jetting arrangement serves to distribute the physical wear equally throughout all parts of the jet tube, resulting in longer jet life.

If four eductors aren't enough, I've even heard of manufacturers utilizing *five* orifice assemblies, fed by a single manifold. Frankly, I don't see how this would be much better than four eductors, since this would make it even more difficult to match the dredge pump's gallonage output to the total surface area of the five eductors, to insure proper volume and pressure for the emerging jet streams.

Over the years, several dredge manufacturers have constructed power-jets with two orifice assemblies welded onto a metal tube, for use with "twin engine" dredges. In fact, one well-known manufacturer currently does this with their eight-inch surface dredge, which uses two lightweight 16 H.P. single cylinder pump and engine assemblies instead of one fantastically heavy automobile engine. In practice, each pump and engine feeds its own orifice assembly, re-

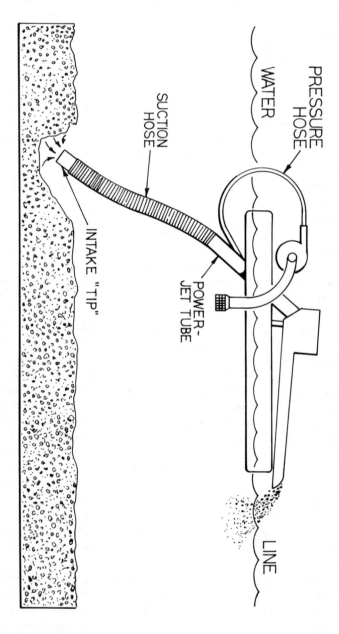

PRESSURE HOSE

WATER

SUCTION HOSE

POWER-JET TUBE

INTAKE "TIP"

LINE

Figure 3—Power-jet type of surface dredge.

sulting in overall suction power just as good as if one "heavy-weight" engine were employed. This same principle can be used to power smaller dredges, as well. I know of more than one gold-dredger who uses two 8 H.P. pump and engine assemblies to power a six-inch surface rig, with excellent results.

One of the more significant features of the power-jet — be it single, double, four or five eductor — is its ability to create noticeably more vacuum than a suction nozzle. Extensive testing with vacuum gauges has proved the power-jet to be more efficient, and the reasons for this are twofold: (1) A power-jet, since it utilizes pure vacuum to *lift* the stream gravel to the surface from above, does not have to contend with "upward resistance" as is encountered with a suction nozzle, which loses much of its orifice power pushing the stream gravel up through the suction hose from the intake end; (2) since a power-jet is located at the back of the sluice box, the pressure hose carrying water from the pump to the orifice (or manifold) only has to be four or five feet long. Remember this fact — the *shorter* the length of pressure hose through which water must travel from the pump, the lesser the distance over which the water encounters *friction,* resulting in greater volume (and, thereby, orifice pressure) at the point of delivery.

Power-jets and suction nozzles are the two dominant eduction devices used to power surface-type gold dredges, yet there is a *third* style of jet that sees use today. This eductor consists of two sections of steel tubing, one flared out to a larger diameter so that the other will fit into it, and is known as a "circle," or "ring" jet. This jet still works on the Venturi principle, although the orifice system is totally different from anything we have studied so far.

In a circle-jet, the orifice is a complete circle, or ring, formed when the two lengths of tubing are almost — but not quite — butted together. One piece of tubing is straight — we will call it the *inner section* — and it is inserted into the flared portion of the second length, which we'll call the *outer section.* The inner section is inserted into the outer section almost up to the beginning of the flare, leaving a small gap that forms the circular orifice. The back end of the outer section of tubing consists of a flange with a rubber gasket, and this acts as a seal to close off the overlap where the inner section is inserted. (Figure 4)

As you can see by studying Figure 4, there exists a sort of "chamber" between the inner and outer sections. In the middle of the outer section is an inlet for the water flow from the pump, and as this water enters the chamber it immediately fills up the space between the inner and outer sections of tubing. Since it has no place else to go, the water is squeezed down and forced out of the circle gap formed at the near-junction of the inner and outer sections. When the water is compressed down in this manner and forced through the gap, vacuum is created at the back end of the inner section that protrudes from the sealing flange. It is here where a length of suction hose is attached.

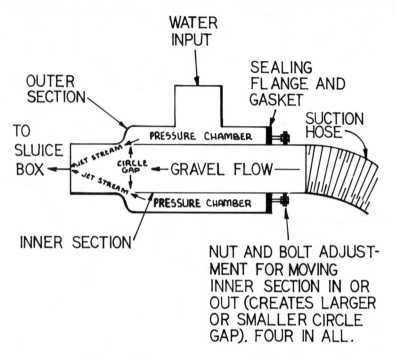

WATER INPUT

OUTER SECTION

SEALING FLANGE AND GASKET

SUCTION HOSE

TO SLUICE BOX

PRESSURE CHAMBER

JET STREAM

CIRCLE GAP

JET STREAM

←GRAVEL FLOW—

PRESSURE CHAMBER

INNER SECTION

NUT AND BOLT ADJUST-MENT FOR MOVING INNER SECTION IN OR OUT (CREATES LARGER OR SMALLER CIRCLE GAP). FOUR IN ALL.

Figure 4—Diagram of "circle," or "ring" jet.

So far we've been talking about dredges that send the river gravel up to a floating sluice box on the surface of the stream for processing and concentration. The surface dredge, to be sure, is the most efficient and practical unit for underwater mining today, but it is actually the outgrowth of an earlier type of dredge known as a *submersible,* or more commonly, an "underwater dredge."

An underwater dredge is a special device which is completely submerged and operated under the surface of the stream in which you are working. It consists of a suction nozzle welded onto a long, outward-tapered metal tube with a removable riffle tray at the back end. (Figure 5) This type of dredge still works off the pressure hose from the pump output, but only in this case the gravel is not sent up to the surface through a long length of suction hose. Because of this fact, the underwater dredge can move a slightly larger amount of gravel than a surface dredge with the same size intake. To explain this I must bring up hydromechanic theory.

When a mixture of gravel, rocks and water is being raised to the surface of a stream via a suction hose, it is only the actual rock and gravel components that are being lifted; the weight of the water inside the suction hose is equal to the weight of the water outside in the stream. So long as you are moving and transporting gravel and water from one point to another *completely underwater* (as is the

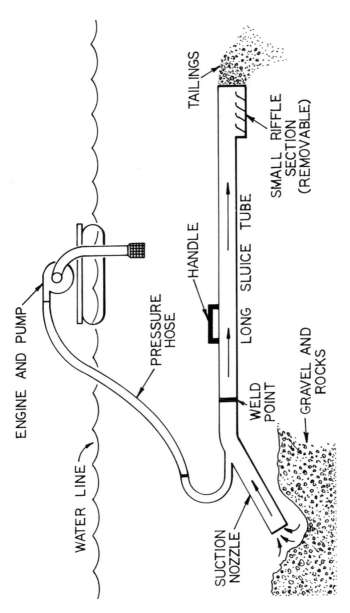

ENGINE AND PUMP

WATER LINE

PRESSURE HOSE

HANDLE

TAILINGS

SMALL RIFFLE SECTION (REMOVABLE)

LONG SLUICE TUBE

WELD POINT

GRAVEL AND ROCKS

SUCTION NOZZLE

Figure 5—Diagram of underwater dredge.

case with the underwater dredge), you will run into relatively little difficulty. But once you lift the material in the suction hose *above the surface of the stream,* even a matter of inches, you are lifting not only the gravel components but also the *water* inside the suction hose which was neutral in weight when it was originally down under the surface. The lifting of water above its "base level" robs the eduction system of a noticeable percentage of its power, but the underwater dredge is not subject to this law and will therefore deliver maximum suction and gravel intake.

The underwater dredge is a very popular unit due to its portability, as the entire dredge consists of engine and pump, flotation tube, pressure hose, pump intake assembly and the actual underwater dredging tube itself. Because of its portability, the underwater dredge is often packed into a remote area for sampling to determine if an area is worthy of a larger, surface-type dredge. The underwater dredge is not usually preferred for *serious* mining work due to the small riffle tray at the discharge end of the dredging tube. The shorter and narrower the riffle tray, the less surface area there is to catch the particles of gold. When working a rich section of river bottom, the prospector will invariably turn to a surface dredge, as this type of rig with its larger sluice box will trap well over 95 per cent of the gold that enters it.

It is quite common for a gold-diver to own *both* a surface and an underwater dredge, and run them from the same engine and pump by switching the pressure hose from the orifice of one dredge to the eduction device on the other. When the dredger wishes to move large amounts of "overburden," he will use the underwater dredge. Though the riffle section is small, he will not lose much gold due to the fact that most overburden is practically barren of the yellow stuff anyway. The dredger will usually remove the overburden a little at a time, stopping every hour or so to check the material in the riffle tray. When he suddenly runs into a section of gravel that contains a larger percentage of gold, the dredger will switch his pressure hose to the surface rig and run the gravel up to the large sluice box topside for better recovery.

The newest innovation in underwater mining equipment is the "sub-surface" dredge, which combines the best features of the surface unit with the desirable characteristics of an underwater rig. A sub-surface dredge consists of a specially designed sluice box suspended under the surface of the stream by cables or chains from a flotation rigging and power unit above. At the back end of the sluice box is a power-jet (unmodified) with a length of suction hose extending from the latter down to the bottom of the stream. (Figure 6)

The sub-surface rig offers the prospector the *larger capacity* of the underwater dredge with the *greater gold recovery* of the surface

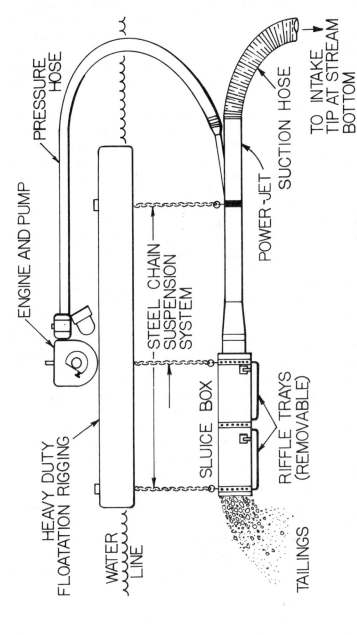

PRESSURE HOSE

ENGINE AND PUMP

HEAVY DUTY FLOATATION RIGGING

WATER LINE

STEEL CHAIN SUSPENSION SYSTEM

SLUICE BOX

RIFFLE TRAYS (REMOVABLE)

TAILINGS

POWER-JET

SUCTION HOSE

TO INTAKE TIP AT STREAM BOTTOM

Figure 6—Diagram of sub-surface dredge.

41

dredge. The sluice box on the sub-surface dredge has a considerably longer riffle tray than that of an underwater rig, enabling it to compete with a surface sluice box from a recovery standpoint. Suction-wise, the sub-surface dredge will pull gravel with the efficiency of an underwater unit due to the fact that the gravel is being routed to its destination entirely beneath the surface of the stream. When one considers the many features of this sophisticated, ultra-modern machine, it is obvious that the sub-surface dredge will play a large and important role in underwater mining operations for a long, long time to come.

Suction dredges — be they surface, underwater, or sub-surface — come in a wide variety of styles and sizes, some of them capable of moving and processing more gravel than others. One of the big problems confronting the beginning dredger is how to select a rig that will do the type of job he has in mind. If *you're* not quite sure as to how to choose the right dredge for your own needs, you'll have to ask yourself about the kinds of places where you'll be using the dredge. Will you be dredging just for the fun of it, near one of the many river campgrounds? Will you be attempting the recovery of gold from small crevices right at the edge of a shallow stream? Or will you be going after the really *big* gold which often lies under ten or twenty feet of overburden at the very bottom of a large river? Whatever type of dredging operation you have in mind, you'll have to understand that one very important characteristic of a suction dredge that seems to cause a great deal of confusion among neophyte underwater prospectors. This is the dredge's "inch-rating."

When you see a gold dredge being advertised, say, as a "1 ½-inch" dredge, this means that the inside diameter of the suction hose (in the case of a surface dredge) that goes up to the back of the sluice box is 1 ½ inches. It is *not* the diameter of the suction nozzle or intake tip, as many people believe. The diameter of the suction nozzle, or tip, is anywhere from ¼ inch to a full inch *less* than the inside diameter of the suction hose, so that rocks of the same size as the hose's inside diameter won't pass through the intake to continually clog up the hose. In the case of our 1 ½-inch dredge, the diameter of the intake would be approximately 1 ¼ inches across. An underwater dredge is also rated according to inches, but in this case it is the inside diameter of the suction nozzle, excluding the reduced intake, that counts. A sub-surface dredge uses the same inch-rating as the surface rig.

The inside diameter of the suction hose (or suction nozzle, in an underwater dredge) also has direct relation to the amount of gravel that the dredge will move per hour. Again I must bring up hydromechanics by quoting this basic principle: "If you double the inside diameter of a section of pipe or hose, you increase the carrying capacity by a factor of four." Say, for example, that your dredge is a 1½-inch model. Such a dredge usually employs a small one horsepower engine, and if this is the case, you could move about one cubic yard of gravel per hour. If you doubled your hose diameter to three inches and added a larger engine and pump, you could move about four cubic yards per hour. If you doubled that to six inches (with a correspondingly larger engine and pump), you could move about sixteen yards an hour and so on up the line.

In many advertisements for gold dredges you will read quotations stating, perhaps, that a particular dredge is capable of moving "sixteen cubic yards of gravel per hour." Quite frequently a prospector will tell me he bought a dredge and that it didn't move *nearly* the quoted hourly yardage. Sometimes the miner will be irate, and perhaps he has a right to be. To clear up this matter once and for all, I offer the following information: "Yardage-per-hour figures are based on the amount of loose, classified (evenly sized) gravel that a dredge's intake is capable of picking up in one hour's time. Yardage-per-hour figures relate the *absolute maximum* amount of material the dredge will pull under the *most ideal conditions.*"

When dredge manufacturers conduct tests on yardage capability, they commonly employ sorted, screened gravel roughly the size of roofing granules. Unfortunately, the gravels to be found on the bottoms of rivers and creeks are *not* sorted and classified according to size. You may have half-inch pebbles imbedded between six-inch-wide rocks, and if the rocks are larger than the size of your intake, you will have to move them aside by hand. In gravel such as this there is no way on earth for a dredge to move the quoted maximum capacity; in fact, you'll be doing fantastic if you move *half* the quoted capacity!

Another area of confusion among the uninitiated is figures relating to depths of operation, or more simply, "How deep can I go before I need a more powerful dredge?" This is where engine size, pump output and a whole mess of other variables come together. Like yardage-per-hour figures, numbers relating to depth capability need clarification, and here is a simplified explanation: "Published depth figures relate the maximum depth capability at which a given dredge will effectively operate and still deliver gravel to the surface."

There are three principle factors that enter into the depth capability of a gold dredge. They are: (1) temperature and altitude of the area in which the dredge is being run; (2) the upward speed of water travel inside the suction hose, and (3) the operating speed of the engine and pump. Let's study these factors more closely.

Whether we realize it or not, the performance of a gasoline engine is very definitely affected by altitude and temperature, and in the case of small "lawnmower" type engines commonly used on gold dredges this is no exception. A general rule to follow is, "For each 1,000 feet of altitude above sea level, the power of the dredge engine will decrease by 3½ per cent. For each ten degrees of temperature above sixty degrees Fahrenheit, engine power will decrease by one per cent."

Let's create a hypothetical situation. We are dredging in a river at the bottom of a very deep canyon, with ridges over two thousand feet high. The altitude of our dredging spot is 3,000 feet above sea level, and it is a very hot summer day; the air temperature is 100 degrees at the bottom of the canyon. Taking into account our engine characteristics, we will lose 10.5 per cent of our engine power simply because we are 3,000 feet above sea level. Second, we lose another four per cent because the air temperature is forty degrees above the sixty-degree mark. This totals up to a 14.5 per cent loss of engine power and gallonage per minute without our hardly being aware of it. The less gallonage of water per minute going through the eduction device, the less lifting power we have at our disposal.

Another factor entering into depth capability — and a very important one, I might add — is the upward speed at which the water and rocks are traveling through the suction hose. The actual speed in feet per second is difficult to pin down, because one type of stream gravel may be coarser or finer than another and require an engine throttle adjustment for greater or lesser speed. In either case, if the speed of water going through the suction hose is not great enough, many of the lighter gravel components will actually "stall out" and spin around in a state of suspension inside the hose. When such a condition exists, as in cases of dredging at maximum depth ranges, the engine will have to be opened up all the way in order to force the absolute maximum amount of water out of the pump and into the eduction device; doing this will create the extra surge of power needed to alleviate a stall-out.

And that brings us to the last major factor entering into depth capability — *engine speed.* The maximum depth potential quoted by a specific manufacturer for one of his dredges can usually be attained only when the power unit is run at — or in excess of — the engine manufacturer's recommended operating speed. This speed is commonly 3,600 RPM, but the average dredge engine will run slower (at a speed of approximately 3,200 RPM) due to the load being backed up on the water pump by the restricted jet orifice. It is a known fact that a lawnmower-type engine — running with *no load at all* — will reach speeds in excess of 3,600 RPM. In order to gain the absolute maximum depth potential from your dredge, you will usually find it necessary to run your engine at a speed of 3,600 RPM or greater *with* the pressure load being backed up on the pump. This higher speed is attained by adjusting the governor device and/or the throttle on the engine.

Any time an engine is run in excess of the manufacturer's recommended operating speed (i.e., 3,600 RPM), it should be operated on an *intermittent basis only*. If you think it will be necessary for you to dredge at maximum depths for extended periods of time, I'd advise you to consult the people from whom you'll be purchasing your dredge. They can recommend an engine and pump which is more powerful than one found on a "stock" model, which will enable you to work at deeper-than-normal depths on a continuous basis. Let's suppose, for a moment, that bedrock in the "hole" you intend to dredge is thirty feet down. You can purchase a stock dredge that will pull satisfactorily — with the engine running at nominal speeds — while working your way down through the overburden, but as you started to approach the twenty-foot mark, you would probably find it necessary to open up your engine all the way in order to maintain good suction. From here on, all the way down to bedrock, your power unit will be running faster than the speeds it was engineered for, putting a great strain on the engine. If that's not enough, consider this: what if bedrock should turn out to be *deeper* than thirty feet? Not only would your engine be running under a strained condition, but your *very suction* would start to drop off as you went below the thirty-foot mark.

The entire situation just described could be alleviated by purchasing a dredge with a power unit *larger* than that found on a stock model. For example, if you were to purchase a dredge capable of pulling, say, from *fifty-foot depths* on a continuous basis, you wouldn't have to run your engine at excessive speeds. You could operate the engine in the general neighborhood of 3,200 RPM and vacuum your way to the thirty-foot level "full speed ahead." And once you finally got there, you would have all the power you'd ever need.

Even though your dredge may be capable of pulling from depths of thirty feet, this doesn't necessarily mean that you'll be dredging at that great a depth. As I stated in an earlier Chapter, most recreational gold-diving is done in less than ten feet of water, and in an operation such as this you should very rarely — if ever — find it necessary to overpower your engine. The one time you might find it necessary is if you're dredging at exceptionally high altitudes in which the power of your engine will decrease greatly. You will then have to "goose up" the engine's RPM to get the additional gallonage to satisfactorily power the eduction device. If this isn't enough, consult the people from whom you purchased your dredge about getting an engine and pump that will deliver a substantial gallonage even at reduced speeds. And while we're on this subject, let me say there are no deep dark secrets concerning the so-called "high-altitude" dredges that are on the market today. Basically, they are dredges equipped with an engine two or three horsepower larger than those found on normal, stock models. But remember one more thing — as you increase the size of your engine, you increase the *weight*, and this can make the difference between success and failure when it comes time to pack a dredge into the back country.

At this point in time we have discussed such matters as the workings of a suction gold dredge, various eduction devices, the three common types of dredges, and so forth. I realize my previous explanations have involved a goodly amount of heavy, technical data that must surely have you crawling the walls, so let's leave "technical tedium" behind, for a while, as we take a look at gold-dredging equipment of the 1970's. We will primarily discuss surface dredges, starting out with the smallest and working our way up to the larger, more powerful rigs that can literally drain a river dry. (Would you believe a small creek???)

Some of the most popular suction dredges on the market today are the small, compact "mini-dredges" which are manufactured by a number of companies. These rigs are called mini-dredges because they are, indeed, small. The total weight of such a unit — including engine, pump, float, sluice box, and all suction and pressure hose — is approximately thirty-five pounds. The lightness in weight of the mini-dredge is due principally to the small size of the engine and pump. The power unit on a mini-dredge is usually a one horsepower, "two-cycle" job with a pump that puts out around 55 gallons of water per minute to a power-jet eduction device. Believe it or not, the entire engine and pump weighs under ten pounds! (A very popular style of mini-dredge is shown in Figure 7.)

The mini-dredge is commonly offered in a 1½-inch configuration, but there are variations; some dredges with a two-inch intake can still be called mini-dredges. Whatever the actual size, the mini-dredge is a popular unit for backpacking into remote areas where gold is often more plentiful. The small intake of the mini-dredge makes it very easy to work shallow crevices which often are rich in gold. If a dredger wishes to sample heavily graveled areas for traces of gold, he may do so with the mini-dredge, as most of these rigs are capable of moving up to one cubic yard of material per hour. It should be noted, however, that the mini-dredge is *not* designed for an all-out attack on large gravel bars. Places such as this may require the removal of dozens of cubic yards of material a day, and the mini-dredge cannot perform this task.

The next step up from a 1½-inch dredge brings us to a unit that shows promise of a great future — this is the two-inch dredge. (Figure 8) Two-inch dredges move substantially more gravel than a 1½-inch dredge, yet weigh only a few pounds more. Most two-inch dredges are powered by a 1½-horsepower two-cycle engine, with a

Figure 7—A very popular style of surface dredge is the small, lightweight 1½-inch "mini-dredge." This unit is primarily designed for sampling and working shallow crevices. (Photo courtesy of Keene Industries.)

Figure 8—A dredge that has recently entered the mining scene (recently, that is, when compared to other sizes) is the two-inch surface rig. Depending upon the manufacturer, it weighs anywhere from thirty to fifty pounds, and moves substantially more gravel than a 1½-inch dredge. (Photo courtesy of Keene Industries.)

pump that delivers approximately 75 gallons of water per minute to a power-jet eductor. A two-inch dredge usually comes with ten feet of suction hose, although one manufacturer furnishes a fifteen foot length; two-inch dredges are capable of moving anywhere from two to three cubic yards of gravel per hour. These nifty little dredges weigh in at anywhere from thirty to fifty pounds, depending upon the manufacturer and the type of floatation arrangement employed.

Going up the line, the next dredge in our "rogue's gallery" of underwater mining equipment would be a 2½-inch rig. (Figure 9) The 2½-inch dredge sees wide use in gold streams of the Western United States for two principal reasons. First, it is a comparatively lightweight unit which falls in the 75- to 100-pound range. Second, these rigs are capable of pulling a pretty fair amount of gravel for their size and weight — most 2½-inch dredges are capable of moving up to four cubic yards of gravel per hour. The engine employed on a 2½-inch dredge will usually be one of three or four horsepower in size, with a pump that puts out approximately 100 gallons of water per minute. The type of eductor used on a 2½-inch dredge is usually a power-jet, although there are many thousands of older 2½-inch rigs still in circulation that employ suction nozzles. A 2½-inch dredge will usually come equipped with ten feet of suction hose, although such units can pull from depths of twenty feet with the addition of extra suction and, in the case of suction nozzle rigs, pressure hose.

As we leave the realm of 1½-, two-, and 2½-inch dredges, we start looking at units that are considered to be "workhorse rigs" by underwater prospectors. A workhorse rig, simply, is a dredge capable of moving a fairly large amount of gravel per hour from deeper-than-normal depths. (Anything over ten feet down is considered "deeper than normal.") The first such dredge in the "workhorse" category is a three-inch dredge. (Figure 10)

A three-inch dredge is a unit capable of moving approximately eight cubic yards of gravel per hour from depths of up to thirty feet. The size of the engine on a three-inch dredge will usually be five horsepower, with a pump that delivers in the neighborhood of 175 gallons of water per minute. Virtually every three-inch dredge I've ever seen employs a power-jet eduction device. The nice thing about a five-horse engine is the fact that it has enough reserve power to run an air compressor, which is driven by a V-belt from a pulley on the engine shaft. A dredge with an air compressor opens up new vistas to the underwater prospector, who can now venture well beneath the surface to move overburden which may conceal rich bedrock crevices.

The next step up from a three-inch dredge brings us to a rig that is widely employed by the *professional* underwater prospector — this is the four-inch dredge. (Figure 11) It is often said that once a

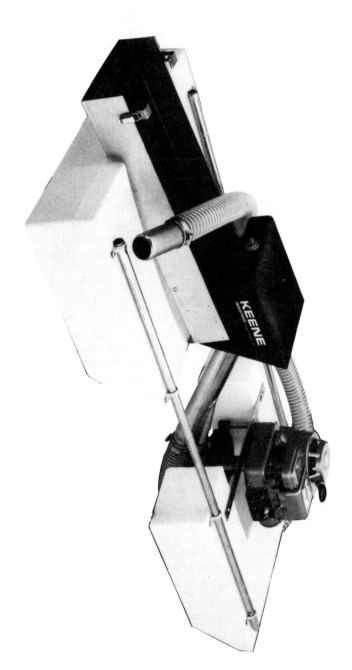

Figure 9—A dredge which has long enjoyed popularity with underwater prospectors is the 2½-inch surface rig; this machine is capable of moving up to four cubic yards of gravel per hour. (Photo courtesy of Keene Industries.)

Figure 10—A three-inch dredge is the first rig that can be called a "workhorse dredge." These rigs can pull from depths as great as thirty feet, and the engine is powerful enough to drive an air compressor for underwater diving. (Photo courtesy of Keene Industries.)

Figure 11—A four-inch surface dredge of the type pictured here is frequently used by the professional gold dredger who needs high capacity together with minimal size and weight. This particular four-inch dredge belongs to the author, and is shown here fully decked out with Hookah diving gear.

dredger uses a four-inch rig he can never go back to a smaller dredge. I can't say this is a truthful statement in all cases, but the four-inch dredge does have its tantalizing features. One of these features is capacity — a four-inch surface dredge using a power-jet eductor is capable of moving upwards of twelve cubic yards of gravel per hour. The engine employed on this type of rig is usually one of seven or eight horsepower in size, with a pump that delivers approximately 200 gallons of water per minute to the eductor. The four-inch surface can truly be called the "dredge in the middle." It is larger and more powerful than the three-inch dredge, moving substantially more gravel, while weighing far less than the next common-sized dredge, the six-inch surface. Many gold-divers run a six-inch *underwater* dredge from the pump output of their four-inch rig, and use it to remove the overburden. When nearing bedrock, they will switch back to the four-inch surface for better gold recovery. The "four-six combination," as it is called, has been widely used by gold-dredgers for over a decade and will always remain popular.

The largest dredge that can still be considered a standardized unit is the six-inch surface rig. (Figure 12) This dredge is for the skilled, serious, professional gold-diver *only*, who is planning on a large-scale operation that may extend over a period of weeks or months. This professional dredge is capable of moving up to sixteen yards of gravel per hour, and is commonly powered by a fifteen or sixteen horsepower industrial engine. Some manufacturers even use a twenty horse engine or larger when extreme depth capability is required. The pump used on a six-inch surface dredge is capable of delivering well over 500 gallons of water per minute to the eduction device, which is almost always a power-jet. The maximum depth capability of a six-inch surface dredge, with a fifteen or sixteen horse engine, is approximately thirty feet.

The dredges described in the preceding paragraphs aren't the only units manufactured, not by any means. It is possible to purchase dredges with eight, ten, twelve, fourteen, and I've even heard of suction dredges with intakes of *twenty-four inches!* Naturally, these units are not for the average individual who is gold-dredging merely for the fun of it. Still, I can't help thinking of the goodies that could be recovered from the bottoms of some of the deep river "holes" that still haven't been touched. It would *take* a "super dredge" to work such a spot, and perhaps one day I'll get the chance to do it.

The information covered in this Chapter thus far should enable you to go out and purchase your first gold dredge. I recommend that you try to buy your dredge — and all other underwater mining equipment — from a reputable manufacturer or dealer who

Figure 12—This is a six-inch surface dredge, a machine designed for the person conducting a large-scale operation for the purpose of recovering paying quantities of gold. These babies are big, to be sure, but, boy, do they ever eat up the gravel! (Photo courtesy of Keene Industries.)

specializes in dredging equipment. Commercially built rigs will always be "state-of-the-art," featuring the latest innovations in pump, orifice, and engine design, as well as being light in weight due to repeated experiments with various types of construction materials. You can, of course, build your own suction dredge, but if this is your intention, I can tell you right now that you'll have difficulty in trying to find specifications to follow. About the only things I can suggest would be to study the various components of a dredge that's owned by a friend, or else visit a dealer who sells dredging equipment and study the various models on display. If you do the latter, however, let me make one suggestion — bring along your own tape measure, pencil, and notebook! Now, most dealers don't mind if you scrutinize their equipment — after all, how else will you know whether or not you'll be wanting to buy it? But they *are* apt to get a bit irritated if you ask them for pencil, paper, and tape measure so that you can copy the various measurements for the purpose of building your own!

Here's another thing to consider — many beginners think that if they buy the engine, pump, sluice box, power-jet or suction nozzle, suction and pressure hoses *separately* and then put them together themselves, they will save a lot of money. This is simply not the case. I've seen many gold dredges built on the "component plan," and in each case the builder probably saved ten or twenty dollars at the most when compared with the cost of a finished unit: he also wound up with a dredge weighing *more* than if he had purchased a standardized, stock rig right off the assembly line. On a different note, the amateur dredge builder may run into difficulty in trying to obtain key components, such as bent sections of tubing for suction nozzles or orifice assemblies for power-jets. Also, persons residing in many smaller communities may have trouble getting even the very *basics*, such as lightweight sheet aluminum for the construction of sluice boxes. Little things like this add up, and in the long run the time you lose in building your own dredge would make it worth your while to purchase a commercially built rig. But if you *still* want to build your own dredge, even after considering these factors, by all means be my guest. As a matter of fact, the experience will do you good!

SECTION B
How to Operate
a Suction Dredge

Right now I'm going to assume that you've bought — or built — yourself a nice, shiny new gold dredge and that you're champing at the bit waiting for summer to come so you can head for "them thar hills" and seek your fortune. This is all fine and dandy, but really, a successful dredging trip begins long before you depart for the hills. The beginning gold-dredger pays meticulous attention to such details as campground reservations, discontinuing the newspaper deliveries for two weeks, having a next-door neighbor look after the family cat, and so forth. But far too few dredgers remember the most important thing of all — that's to *learn how to use your dredge* before you go tramping over Hell's Half Acre in search of the yellow stuff. Well, that's exactly what this Section of Chapter Four is about — how to *use* your dredge.

Before we actually get into operating procedures, let me say that it is very important for the dredger to make a careful examination of his gold dredge before he takes it out and runs it for the first time. This includes an inspection of the power unit, hosing, and flotation rigging to make sure that everything is in proper working order. Let's start out by discussing the one piece of equipment that is the source of more problems (among the inexperienced, that is) than any other. This is the dredge's *engine*.

The four-cycle, portable gasoline engine used on most modern suction dredges is an efficient, hard-working and easily operated piece of equipment that will last for years if you give it a reasonable amount of care. This includes keeping the air filter clean, the spark plug gap free from carbon deposits, and the cooling fins free from debris. But you'd be surprised at the number of gold-divers who will take a dredge into the field secure with the knowledge that their crankcase is filled with fresh, slippery oil. Thornton's Rule Number One: THE CRANKCASE OF A BRAND-NEW ENGINE IS *NEVER* FILLED WITH OIL, AND MUST BE FILLED BY THE PURCHASER. If it seems a little funny for me to have put that last sentence in "caps," it is only to dramatize the importance of the statement. In truth, I've seen more than one new engine "totalled out" by the failure of the user to fill the crankcase with oil before he took it out to run it. As can be expected, this sort of damage is *not* covered by the engine's warranty, so watch it!

And now for Thornton's Rule Number Two: "With any engine used on a gold dredge, it is EXTREMELY important that you follow the manufacturer's instructions as far as oil changing." This is especially true if you're going to be dredging for several weeks or months. The engines used on gold dredges, as you know by now, are of the "lawnmower" type. They were originally designed to be used for perhaps one hour a week at the very most by the average Joe in his backyard, and the sustained running necessary in a dredging situation is extremely hard on such engines if not properly cared for. Most portable gasoline engines require an oil change every 25 hours, which during the course of normal use may occur every six months. In a dredging situation where you may be running your engine for eight to ten hours a day continuous, you will need to change oil *every three days* and certainly no longer than five. When an engine is run for long periods at a time (well, actually, any time it's run *regardless*), tiny slivers of metal will flake off the inside of the engine block and mix themselves with the oil, forming a very destructive substance which doesn't do the insides of the engine much good. People would also be surprised if they saw how fast the oil in a crankcase can turn into a thick, molasses-like sludge which can actually prevent the engine from delivering maximum power. Aside from the necessary oil changes, I advise you to check the oil level in the crankcase at the end of each dredging day, filling it to the point of overflow as needed.

After filling your engine with oil, check parts such as the throttle, the air filter and especially the spark plug. It is a good idea to carry one or two extra plugs with you at all times, or else the necessary tools for periodically cleaning and resetting the gap. This last bit of maintenance need be performed only once a month.

After going over your engine, make an inspection of all the hosing on your dredge. In fact, leaks in the suction and pressure hose system is the number two cause of trouble in the field after the engine is considered. Before running your dredge for the first time, thoroughly go over every foot of hose assembly checking for any holes or thin spots. Should the pressure hose appear to be defective, have it replaced immediately as it may burst when your pump starts sending water through it. And be sure to go over the foot valve and priming hose that delivers water to the pump intake . . . if something is wrong there, you're not going to be doing any dredging at all!

The flotation rigging on a gold dredge is not without its occasional troubles, and it, too, deserves the once-over. Start by checking the inner tube(s) that float the dredge in the stream. Look for pinhole leaks that may develop into full-fledged holes later on, and always carry a tube-patching kit with you on your outings. In case you want to collapse the tubes for easier transportation of the dredge, a bicycle pump is a handy thing to take on your trips so you can re-inflate the tubes at your destination.

If your dredge floats on styrofoam pontoons (also referred to as "billets"), there is little chance of springing a leak in the normal sense, but it is advisable to consult your dealer about possible coating materials for the billets to make them impervious to the effects of water and gasoline. Water leaking into the cell structure of styrofoam can cause a billet to become laden and sink, while gasoline (which frequently spills during the process of filling the gas tank on your engine) actually *disintegrates* styrofoam.

One of the best ways to protect styrofoam billets is to thoroughly cover them with a good ducting tape, and then have them Fiberglased. If you want to take the cheaper way out, you can "glass" them yourself with "boat resin." In either case, it is *not* advisable to glass bare styrofoam itself, because the chemicals in the resin will cause more harm to the billets than the effects of the stream water.

Plastic module flotation systems are impervious to the effects of water and gasoline, and require virtually no care or maintenance. Most modules are molded from a super-tough, cross-link plastic which is virtually indestructible; there is, however, one point which I should mention. On many plastic modules, you will frequently find a small, round hole at some point on the upper surface of the float where all the dredge components are mounted. This is a *ventilation hole*, and it serves a vital function — it allows the module to "breathe," and thereby prevents the module from rupturing due to internal air expansion on a hot day. Leave the ventilation hole as it is, and *do not fill it in!*

' Regardless of whether your flotation rigging consists of inner tubes, billets, or plastic modules, check the metal frame pieces on which the sluice box, engine and pump, etc., are mounted. Make sure all bolt holes in the frame bars line up properly without resorting to force; believe me, there's nothing more aggravating than a float frame that doesn't go together right!

Now that you've checked your dredge over, how about your accessories? Is your diving gear in proper repair? How about your camping gear? Do you have all the necessary screwdrivers, wrenches, etc., for putting your dredge together at your destination? How about the tools necessary for making emergency engine repairs? Do you have enough food and supplies for your intended stay, and, most important, do you have enough of the right type of gasoline for your dredge? Different engines on different dredges may work on only one type of gasoline, such as the "mixed" gas required for the two-cycle engines used on a lot of 1 ½ - and two-inch dredges. If you have such a dredge, be sure to mix your batch of gas *before* you depart on your trip and save precious time in the field. Also, take along a non-breakable measuring cup so that you can mix more fuel in case you need it. Always use regular gas, *never ethyl,* in any type of portable gasoline engine, whether it's to be mixed with oil or not.

Chances are that when you finally arrive in the field, you'll be so excited that you'll just want to plop your dredge into the river and start going to town. But if you first stop and take note of the following operating hints, you'll have a much better time of things on this, your *first* dredging trip and on all your dredging trips to come.

To start off, check and see if your engine, pump and sluice box are all securely mounted onto the flotation rigging. After all, you wouldn't want to see your new dredge go into the drink, would you? It's happened to many an unwary dredger, so play it safe and don't let it happen to you.

One of the most important things to do is to make sure that your dredge is floating *level in the stream* — if it isn't, the gravel going through the sluice box will not make contact with the entire width of the riffles, and a partial loss of gold may result. Problems with dredge leveling are usually confined to dredges that have inner tube flotation systems, as inner tubes will occasionally inflate with a "bubble" in one portion. When the dredge components are mounted on the tubes and floated in the river, the bubble may wind up on one side of the dredge, causing it to float "cockeyed" in the water. This can be alleviated most simply by twisting the troublesome tube so that the bubble is lined up lengthwise with the dredge; this will correct the tendency of the dredge to list sideways. If your dredge floats on styrofoam billets or plastic modules, you shouldn't encounter problems of this nature.

After the main portion of your dredge has been assembled and secured to the flotation rigging, connect all the suction and pressure hose fittings, etc., to the various components shown on the dredge's instruction sheet. Make sure all hose clamps are tightly fastened so they won't vibrate loose during operation. Hose clamps, incidentally, have a habit of getting lost; always carry several extra clamps in each size that's used on your dredge.

The next and certainly one of the most important things to do is to make sure that your pump is correctly primed. A lot of beginning dredgers think that the pump on their dredge is self-priming, which is very rarely the case. The pump must be primed manually by moving the foot valve assembly up and down very rapidly under the surface of the stream; the foot valve assembly is the screened component that's found on the end of your priming hose. Inside the foot valve assembly is a small "flapper" valve, and each time you thrust the assembly down into the water you force the valve open and water will work its way up the priming hose. Each *upward* movement closes the valve so that the water won't leak back down into the river. When priming the pump, it is best to have the pressure hose *loosely connected* to the discharge, as this will allow any air inside the pump housing to be forced out.

Continue the up-and-down "thrusting" motion until water starts to pour from the pump discharge. If your dredge has a transparent pressure hose, you can tell at a glance when the pump is primed, as water will pour from the discharge in a nice, solid flow (minus any air bubbles). Once this occurs, you may tighten the coupler that connects the pressure hose to the discharge.

If you don't have a transparent pressure hose on your dredge, you will have to start the engine to see if the pump is primed. If, upon starting the engine, the pressure hose gets extremely hard and stiff, the pump is correctly primed and water is being properly expelled into the pressure hose. If the pressure hose doesn't get hard, stop the engine IMMEDIATELY. The type of pump that is commonly employed on a suction dredge has a mechanical, spring-loaded "seal" that prevents water leakage from the back of the pump. This seal is usually lubricated by water passing *through* the pump, and if you run your dredge even for a short time with the pump not correctly primed, you may "blow" the seal and have to do a bit of unexpected maintenance in the field. Professional dredgers always carry several spare seals just in case, and this is one habit that *every* dredger should pick up.

With the pump primed, you're ready to commence operations. Start your engine. If your dredge has a suction nozzle and all your suction and pressure hose fittings are correctly attached, you should feel a powerful suction when you place your nozzle under the surface of the stream. If you have suction, you can start dredging. For those of you who have a dredge with a power-jet, you have a few more steps before you can start going after those nuggets.

In order for a power-jet dredge to attain suction, all the air in the power-jet and suction hose must be completely evacuated. What this means is that the entire suction hose and orifice end of the power-jet tube must be completely filled with one unbroken column of water all the way from the intake tip at the river bottom up to a point just above the orifice in the power-jet. If your particular dredge features a "below-water" power-jet (see Figure 13), chances are the orifice will be well down below the water line. If this is the case, then one-half of the requirement is completed. Next, slowly dip

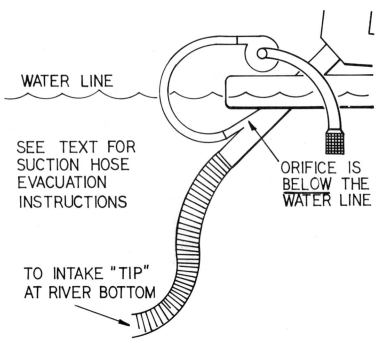

WATER LINE

SEE TEXT FOR
SUCTION HOSE
EVACUATION
INSTRUCTIONS

ORIFICE IS
BELOW THE
WATER LINE

TO INTAKE "TIP"
AT RIVER BOTTOM

Figure 13—Diagram of a "below-water" power-jet.

your suction hose into the water, intake end first. When the entire hose is finally under the water, the air will be evacuated, and you can then hook the free end of the hose onto the orifice end of the power-jet and start dredging.

There are several manufacturers of dredging equipment who put out power-jet dredges on which the jet-tube is positioned out of the water. There are two basic styles of "above-water" power-jet dredges, and they are shown in Figures 14-A and B). One type of dredge has the power-jet mounted on top of the flotation rigging (Figure 14-A), while the other has the power-jet hanging in mid-air off the rear end of the dredge (Figure 14-B). On either type of dredge, your suction hose will be filled with water only up to the point where the hose is sticking up out of the river. From that point on, all the way up to the orifice in the power-jet, the suction hose will be filled with air that will have to be manually evacuated. Depending on the style of your dredge, there are several different ways of doing this. In *all* cases, place the "intake tip" end of the suction hose in the water with the free end attached to the input of the power-jet.

If you have a dredge with an above-water power-jet of the type shown in Figure 14-A, there are two means of manually evacuating

ABOVE-WATER POWER-JET MOUNTED ON FLOATATION RIGGING

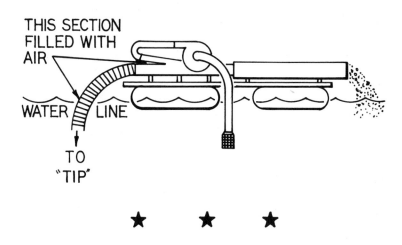

THIS SECTION FILLED WITH AIR

WATER LINE

TO "TIP"

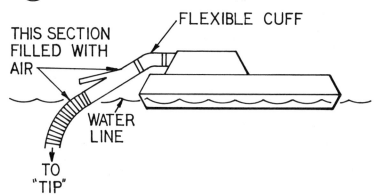

ABOVE-WATER POWER-JET HANGING OFF REAR OF DREDGE

FLEXIBLE CUFF

THIS SECTION FILLED WITH AIR

WATER LINE

TO "TIP"

ON ANY DREDGE WITH AN "ABOVE-WATER" POWER-JET, THE SUCTION HOSE WILL BE FILLED WITH WATER ONLY UP TO THE POINT WHERE IT EMERGES FROM THE RIVER. THE ABOVE-WATER PORTION IS FILLED WITH AIR WHICH MUST BE **MANUALLY** EVACUATED (SEE TEXT).

Figure 14—Two common examples of "above-water" power-jets.

the suction hose; the method to use depends upon whether or not your sluice has a "swing-open" baffle box. If your baffle box *does* swing open, hook the output end of the power-jet tube onto the back of the sluice. Swing open the baffle box and start your engine running at half speed. A surge of water will come through the power-jet and through the collar that connects the jet with the input of the baffle box. Place your hand inside the baffle box and over the collar entrance to form a blockage; the water going through the power-jet will hit your hand and start to flow *backwards* through the suction hose, blowing the air in the hose out the end which is under the water. When bubbles stop coming from the "tip" end of the suction hose, you will know that the air is evacuated. Now all you do is close and latch the baffle box, put your engine on full speed and start dredging.

If your dredge has an above-water power-jet *without* a swing-open baffle box, make all the necessary hose connections with the exception of hooking the power-jet to the input of the baffle box; leave the jet-tube lying on top of the flotation rigging. Again, you should start your engine running at half speed. Pick up the power-jet and get a grip on it with *one* hand while using the other to block the output end. From here on, the evacuation procedure is the same as that for a dredge with a swing-open baffle box — the water going through the power-jet will hit your hand and flow backwards through the system to blow air out of the "tip" end at the stream bottom. When the air is evacuated, remove your hand from the end of the power-jet and couple it to the collar that leads into the baffle box. You can now throttle your engine up to full speed and start dredging.

If your above-water power-jet hangs out over the river in the manner illustrated in Figure 14-B, the manual evacuation procedure is a snap. Connect all the suction and pressure hose fittings to their proper places, and couple the power-jet to the back of the sluice box. This time start your engine running at normal speed. Next, use physical pressure to force the intake end of the power-jet just far enough under the surface of the stream for the orifice to be slightly submerged (a mere inch is enough). As soon as the orifice is submerged, there will be a linkup of the water in the suction hose with the water going through the orifice, and suction will commence instantly. When this occurs, let the power-jet spring back up into its normal position; you are ready for business!

If you own a dredge with an above-water power-jet, it is important for you to remember the following fact: any time you shut down the engine on your dredge, air is going to enter the connecting collar at the entrance to the sluice's baffle box and will force the water inside the power-jet tube and suction hose *back down to the water level of the stream,* thereby necessitating the manual re-evacuation of the suction hose each time the dredge is restarted. This is something that very few beginning dredgers realize, and naturally, they're going to be dismayed when they run into this situation in the field.

On most above-water power-jet dredges, the jet-tube is lined up on the same horizontal plane as the sluice box, and the full fury of the power-jet's water flows shoots directly down the "riffle plane" with very little baffling. Because of this, the speed of the current in the sluice box of an above-water power-jet dredge is extremely fast, and it is not unusual to have "whitecaps" rolling down the length of the sluice box. This highly undesirable turbulence can result in a noticeable loss of fine gold. The condition just mentioned is not a problem on a below-water power-jet dredge which has the jet-tube entering the sluice on a conventional forty-five-degree angle, because the baffle box on this type of dredge is more efficient and greatly reduces the force of the water shooting out of the discharge end of the power-jet.

On any dredge that employs an above-water power-jet, it is important that all the hose clamps used for securing the suction and pressure hoses to the back of the jet be tightened down as firmly as possible. If air is accidentally pulled into a power-jet anywhere *before* the orifice, a noticeable decline in suction may result; an inexperienced dredger might beat his brains out trying to think of where the problem lies. On a power-jet dredge with the orifice below the water line this is not a problem, as a tiny amount of water leaking in at the suction or pressure hose connection isn't going to do anything except add a little *more* water. But air, that's another story. In order to get suction, the jet stream emerging from the orifice must push against *water* in the main body of the power-jet; any air in the tube is going to interfere with the jet stream's ability to displace this water.

When running any type of power-jet dredge, it is advisable to keep the intake tip under the surface of the stream at all times. If you lift the tip *above* the water line, you are going to pull in air and thereby break the continuous column of water inside the suction hose and power-jet tube. A small "gulp" of air pulled into the system won't hurt matters, but if you take in air for several seconds, this may be enough to stop your suction. If this happens, you may find it necessary to re-evacuate your suction hose.

Before you settle down to any really serious dredging operations, you should make a check of your sluice box to see if the *degree of slope* is correct for the type of gravel you're running. In all cases, the sluice box should be adjusted so that when gravel, rocks and water are running through the sluice, the top half of the riffles is visible at all times. If you can't see the top portion of the riffles, the angle of the sluice isn't steep enough to cause the lighter waste material to flow out. Your box will then load up with lighter "junk" gravel while allowing the *new* gravel coming up from below to pour right over the waste material without even contacting the riffles, which at this point are just plain *buried.* This is one of the few ways you can lose gold from your sluice box.

Now let's look at the other side of the coin. If you look into the sluice box and see the entire riffle exposed, the angle of the sluice is *too steep* and will allow the gravel to pour out of the box very easily without making adequate riffle contact. Once again, a loss of gold is possible. The trick is to find a happy medium — that is, a point where the degree of slope allows the gravel to make adequate contact with the riffles while allowing the lighter waste materials to pour out of the box. It has been my experience that a slope of *one-half inch per linear foot* of sluice box will usually do the trick. Of course, there will always be variables. If you should run into a situation where the normal rules don't apply, remember this — the coarser and heavier the gravels going through a sluice box, the *greater* the degree of slope; the finer the gravels, the *lesser* the slope. To adjust the slope of your sluice box, lift the box from its "level-rod" support and lay it on the float frame. Place the leveling rod into a higher or lower set of holes in the sluice box support brackets which are found on the flotation frame. Re-position the sluice box on the leveling rod and you're ready for action.

Now that you're ready to start dredging, I should make note of one final consideration — the running speed of your engine. Even though the typical four-cycle dredge engine will develop about 3,200 RPM when driving the eduction device, YOU DON'T NECESSARILY HAVE TO RUN THE ENGINE THIS FAST. Many commercially built suction dredges are overpowered to some degree, and are capable of delivering good suction power at speeds lower than 3,200 RPM. (An exception to this rule would be small 1 ½- and two-inch "mini-dredges" which use two-cycle engines; these rigs should always be run at full speed — approximately 5,000 RPM — to maintain good suction.) Here's another thing to bear in mind: no matter what the size of your dredge, it is possible to blow fine, flaky gold *out of your sluice box* by running your eduction system at too high a speed! Many dredgers (including this author) like to put "hand throttles" on their dredge engines so that the engine speed may be varied by a simple wrist movement. By all means, *experiment,* and select a speed setting that (1) develops adequate suction power, (2) without creating unnecessary turbulence in the sluice box, while (3) maintaining a proper "eddying" action in the riffles. You won't learn to run a dredge this way overnight, but don't worry — it will come to you after a few days' time spent in the field.

CHAPTER FIVE

Homework—
The Gold-Dredgers'
Ticket to Success

All of us can look back at our high school and college days and instantly recall some of the more pleasant aspects of this period. Let your mind drift back a number of years, and you'll probably think of chums you used to hang around with, games you used to play at recess, the time you played the lead role in the school play, and other nostalgic elements too numerous to mention. Yes, there were many enjoyable aspects of our schoolyears, but when you ask anyone about the one particularly *bad* aspect of school, he will probably say HOMEWORK.

Most of us have been out of school for quite a few years now, and homework is behind us. But did you know that homework — and a goodly amount of it, at that — is a *prerequisite* for successful underwater prospecting? True, it's not the type of homework you used to hate so much in school, but nevertheless it involves the study of such sophisticated subject material as topographic and geologic maps, detailed geological reports and treatises, and historical accounts concerning mining activities in a given geographical area. This type of homework also involves a certain amount of *assumption* on the part of the would-be gold-dredger, as geologic and historical accounts frequently have gaps in continuity which must be filled in by the prospector to the best of his ability.

The beginning gold-dredger will often find it extremely difficult to decide upon an area in which to prospect. There are *so many* rich areas to choose from in our Western mining states one is literally tempted to take a map, close his eyes, stick out his index finger, touch it to the map and wherever it lands . . . voila! Actually, there are far better ways of determining which areas are suitable for successful gold-dredging, and perhaps the best is to consult the highly detailed geological "reports" published by the "Divisions of Mines and Geology" of the various mining states. A geological report is an engrossing, all-encompassing study of a specific mining region of limited size. A report usually will be done on an area that was (or still is) a large and famous producer of mineral commodities, including metals and minerals other than gold. Quite frequently, a geological report will be a previously unpublished dissertation for a geologist's doctorate degree, and this assures the reader of the most accurate and factual information possible. Every effort is made to include in the report information on local geology and rock types, fault structures, major mines and their locations (together with the conditions which formed the deposit of mineral in these mines), the historical background of the mining district, and occasionally, listings of individual mining claims with the names and addresses of the owners. If you know what to look for when reading a geological report, you can obtain a literal "gold mine" (excuse the pun) of information to help you in your prospecting efforts. Let's look at a few of the ways a geological report can help the underwater prospector.

A geological report goes a long way in presenting the detailed conditions which led to the deposition of mineral commodities in the region being studied. By reading the descriptions of the various mines mentioned in a report, you can gain valuable knowledge as to the varying geologic conditions which created that particular mineral deposit. What you should then do is obtain a *geologic map* (more on that later) of the area in question and look for those same conditions in the area you're interested in prospecting. For example, let's suppose a hypothetical gold deposit that yielded millions was located on a "fault zone" where serpentine and slate-phyllite rock formations came together. It would be wise to look for the same, identical geologic formation at a point *upstream* from the area you intend to dredge; so long as the fault zone you personally located is in the approximate area of the bonanza deposit, there is a reasonable chance for your fault zone to also contain gold. Any gold veins on the fault zone deposit would erode down into the streamflow to be trapped in bedrock pockets and gravel bar deposits. If you were to set up your dredge and start working very near the fault zone, you could conceivably come up with coarse gold that had just eroded from the vein.

Some of the more elaborate geologic reports (particularly those that cover an entire county) will give fantastically detailed descriptions of individual mining claims. The nature of these deposits will be discussed, together with information as to the specific mineral(s) found, the mining methods employed, the history of production, the current status of the claim and, when known, the name and address of the legal owner. Imagine the possibilities! A dredger, for example, can study production records of various river claims to see which ones yielded the most gold. He then can make an effort to determine whether the claim is still up to date or else reverted back to the Public Domain. If the latter holds true, the dredger can possibly refile the claim himself and pick up where the original owners left off. There is a good chance they left something! (The process of tracking down a mining claim to determine its validity will be discussed in great detail in Chapter 14.)

A good geologic report will contain maps of ancient, gold-bearing river systems that used to flow tens of millions of years ago. These old rivers are known commonly as "Tertiary channels," Tertiary being the geologic period in history during which they flowed. Tertiary channels occupied different streambeds than those of today's drainage systems, and over the passing of eons the Tertiary river systems were buried by vast beds of volcanic debris. A couple of million years ago the rivers and streams we know today began to cut through the beds of their ancient counterparts, which flowed approximately forty-five *million* years ago during the Eocene epoch. Wherever a modern-day stream cut through an ancient channel, the gold in the old streambed was released and reconcentrated into the modern rivers. Geologic reports issued on mining districts in Northern and Central California will go into great detail on Tertiary channels, which accounted for a tremendous portion of that state's gold output. These particular maps will be of great interest to the gold-dredger. If you can locate a remote, unprospected area beneath the outcrop of a little-known Tertiary channel, you just might hit a bonanza equal to those discussed a few Chapters back. Unfortunately, it is not within the scope of this book to delve deeply into complex, Tertiary geology, so I shall let you discover this information yourself. There are many excellent geologic reports that cover Tertiary channels, and you will gain much knowledge and experience by studying them *personally*.

After you've discovered and feasted upon every geologic report you can get your hands on, you are ready for something a little different — this is the *geologic map*. A geologic map is not like an ordinary map that shows streets, fire stations, hospitals, city parks and the like. It is a map that utilizes multi-colored printing to illustrate different rock types in a given geographical area. When you first look at a geologic map, you are apt to think, "What an awful mess — how can I understand this?" Actually, reading a geologic map is very simple once you discover the legend which is usually located in the right-hand margin. The legend will explain the meaning of each coloration on the map by stating whether a given color indicates "sedimentary" or "igneous" rock, granite or lava beds, limestone or glacial ice, Tertiary or Pre-Cambrian. Fault zones will also be shown on geologic maps, making them valuable for locating potentially gold-bearing vein structures such as those discussed earlier. Geologic maps can be used for many applications, but to the gold-dredger they have one principal purpose — locating areas where the bedrock is favorable for the entrapment of gold.

The casual gold-dredger will not pay much attention to the type of bedrock in the stream he is working, but the professional underwater prospector will not work an area where the bedrock doesn't have a tendency to develop cracks and fissures which act as natural gold traps. There are three rock types in particular that frequently contain an abundance of natural "riffles," these being slate, phyllite and granite. (I can't promise that *every* area with these bedrock types will be overrun with cracks and crevices; I've seen slate bedrock, for example, that contained one crevice after another, while a mile upstream this same bedrock was as smooth and polished as a headstone!)

The geologic map can be used effectively to locate areas with potentially favorable bedrock, but an on-the-spot inspection is always a necessity. If easily reached "surface bedrock" turns out to be pockety with lots of gold traps, the prospector will stay in the area for a substantial length of time and sample. A section of streambed devoid of cracks and crevices will usually be passed up after several non-productive samples are taken. A prospector will bring in his dredge only if the surface crevices yield color, indicating the existence of even richer crevices at the very bottom of the stream.

A good map, like the proverbial picture, is worth a thousand words. If you wish to learn the lay of the land *before* you journey to a particular area, the "topographic map" is for you. Topographic maps (known commonly as *topo sheets*) are published by the U.S. Geological Survey, and are the most accurate maps in existence. A topo sheet uses a standardized set of symbols to explain different geographic and cultural (man-made) features.

The first thing you will notice when looking at a topographic map is the brown, wavy line pattern that meanders over the entire surface of the map. These are "contour lines," and indicate elevations in feet above mean sea level. At the bottom of the map will be an explanation of the contour lines used on that particular sheet. If the legend says "contour interval forty feet," this means that the difference in elevation between each brown line on the map is forty feet. After you learn to interpret the contour lines on a topographic map, you can determine which land areas are deep canyons, which are mountain peaks, valleys, plateaus, and so forth.

In addition to revealing the shape of the land, topo sheets indicate the changes that man himself has contributed. Topographic maps will show all existing roads, trails, railroads, cities, towns, hamlets, dams, powerhouses, mines and even individual dwellings if they are the sole structure in a given area.

Topographic maps as we've discussed them so far may sound rather dull from the standpoint of the gold-dredger, but hold onto your hats — the best is yet to come! I'm going to show you methods of putting topographic maps to work that most prospectors have never dreamed of.

A while back we talked of contour intervals and how they represent elevations; let's elaborate on this a bit. As you're looking at a topo sheet, you will notice that the contour lines of certain map areas are closer together than in others. Wherever the lines are close to each other, the terrain in that area is very steep; where the contour lines are far apart, the terrain is gentle. A good example of close contour lines would be the representation of a deep river canyon, while separated lines might indicate a gently sloping hill.

How, exactly, can this information help an underwater prospector in his quest for gold? To start off, the prospector can locate deep river canyons with very steep walls simply by observing the spacing between the contour lines. A river canyon with these characteristics, if there are no roads or trails nearby, is very difficult to carry equipment into; the chances are good there will be untouched dredging ground at the bottom. You can go one step further when looking for such localities — you can search for deep river canyons where the close contour lines of the canyon wall go right down to the *edge of the stream*. Areas such as this will have very little shoreline, if any, at the edge of the river, meaning the old-time Chinese miners had no place to divert the river from its bed and work the bedrock clean. If you can locate such a virgin, unmined area and spend a whole summer dredging it, you may find yourself having to hire an armored car to transport your gold to the bank vault. (See Figure 15)

Contour lines can also be used to locate open areas at the bottom of a river canyon that may indicate the presence of wide gravel bars. If contour lines spread *widely apart* upon reaching the bottom

NOTE: THIS IS A HIGHLY-SIMPLIFIED VERSION OF THE FANTASTICALLY COMPLICATED CONTOUR LINE PATTERN FOUND ON A REAL TOPOGRAPHIC MAP; STILL, THIS DIAGRAM SHOULD GIVE YOU THE GENERAL IDEA.

RIVER CANYONS IN WHICH THE WALLS GO RIGHT DOWN TO THE EDGE OF THE STREAM OFFER GREAT POTENTIAL TO THE GOLD-DREDGER, FOR THE OLD-TIME MINERS COULD RARELY "DIVERT" THE STREAM TO LAY BARE THE BEDROCK.

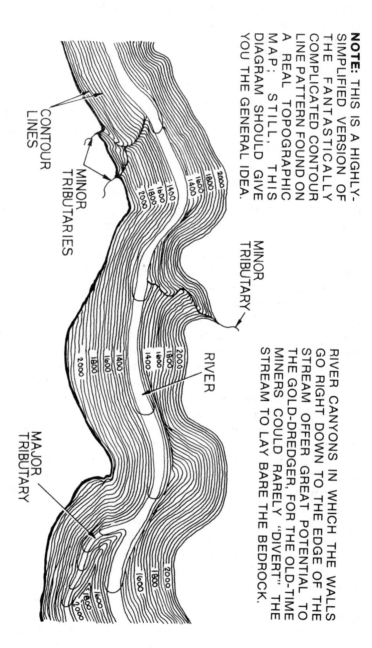

CONTOUR LINES

MINOR TRIBUTARIES

MINOR TRIBUTARY

RIVER

MAJOR TRIBUTARY

Figure 15—Topographic representation of steep-walled river canyon.

of a canyon, you can be reasonably assured that some sort of gravel "beach" will exist. (Figure 16) Professional gold-dredgers will study geologic reports to learn which stream areas were fabulous producers back in the 1850's; with this knowledge in hand they will consult the topographic map to locate gravel bars for possible sampling and evaluation.

The compilers of topo sheets make every effort to show the more noteworthy mining sites on their maps, and if the prospector follows up on the names of these mines, he can learn a great deal of information regarding the presence of gold in the rivers of the area. A detailed topographic map, for example, may reveal a particular mine to have been of the "hydraulic" type where giant water cannons played against banks of gold-bearing Tertiary gravel stranded on top of today's high ridges. By consulting a detailed geologic report on such a mine, you may learn where the *tailings* from this operation were dumped. Chances are they were diverted to a nearby creek to be dumped and, eventually, forgotten. It has been estimated that up to one-third of the gold from hydraulic mines went out with the tailings, and topographic maps will often reveal (in symbols, of course) exactly where these tailings were dumped. Dredgers have recovered many hundreds of ounces of gold from such areas, and there's plenty remaining to be found.

The libraries in the major cities of our Western mining states contain many of the more noteworthy geologic reports, and *larger* libraries even have their own collections of topographic maps. All this information is available to the public — including you, John Q. Golddiver — and I strongly advise you to *use it*. In addition, the various offices of a State's "Division of Mines and Geology" will be the source of staggering amounts of information. Many of these offices contain so much mining literature a person could spend months pouring over their material and still walk away not knowing the half of it. (In the Appendix of this book I will give you the addresses of where to write for geologic publications, topographic maps, etc., that will aid you in your quest for gold.)

While geologic and topographic information is vital to successful research, don't overlook the importance of historical data. Over the years, much useful information has been preserved that can be of aid to the underwater prospector, only you will have to search a little harder to find it. If you are really serious about finding a good dredging spot, I'd advise you to take a trip into the Gold Country and meet the people who know the region best — the local inhabitants. Many present-day citizens of the Western gold districts are actually the descendants of the original argonauts of the 1800's, and they can tell you facts about an area that can't be learned elsewhere. Make every effort to strike up acquaintances with

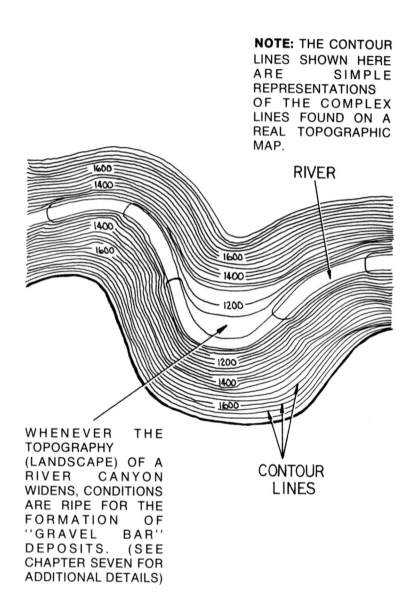

NOTE: THE CONTOUR LINES SHOWN HERE ARE SIMPLE REPRESENTATIONS OF THE COMPLEX LINES FOUND ON A REAL TOPOGRAPHIC MAP.

RIVER

WHENEVER THE TOPOGRAPHY (LANDSCAPE) OF A RIVER CANYON WIDENS, CONDITIONS ARE RIPE FOR THE FORMATION OF "GRAVEL BAR" DEPOSITS. (SEE CHAPTER SEVEN FOR ADDITIONAL DETAILS)

CONTOUR LINES

Figure 16—Topographic representation of river canyon widening.

"old-timers." When present-day old-timers were youngsters back in the early 1900's, the old-timers *they* used to talk to were actually men who had been there during the original Gold Rush! You can pick up all sorts of juicy tidbits in this manner, but never let an old-timer get onto the fact that you're trying to pick his brain; if he gets this impression, he'll "clam up," and you'll never get another word out of him.

The files of local newspapers can provide much useful information, especially the older ones that have been publishing for over a century. During the mining days, these newspapers routinely published stories about significant gold finds of the period, which in many cases included the actual discovery site. One can then follow up such a lead to determine how much work, if any, has since been done at the site.

Many of the more famous mining towns have small "museums" in which old mining artifacts, photographs, letters and documents of the boom period are exhibited. An extraordinary amount of information can be gleaned here, not only from the material on exhibition but from the curator as well. It has been my experience that such persons are extremely proud of the mining heritage of their area, and are more than happy to share it. The curator of a mining museum can hold your attention for hours with stories that never quite made the history books.

I do hope I haven't managed to scare you off after presenting the types of material that should be studied prior to departing on a dredging trip; in reality, the study of geologic reports, geologic maps and topo sheets is not nearly as difficult as it sounds. It will take several hours of reading and concentration, to be sure, but before you realize it you'll be able to tell more about a potential dredging spot than any other gold-diver on your block. In time, you will actually look forward to coming home from a hard day's work and delving into your research material, searching for that one "super-spot" that has to be there . . . just waiting. By consulting the correct study material, by expressing diligence, patience, and persistence, you'll have a better-than-even chance of eventually finding it.

CHAPTER SIX
The Recognition of Gold in its Natural Form

Now that we've pretty much gotten technical matters out of the way, it is time we turn our attention to the actual yellow stuff itself — gold! The rich, romantic history of this cherished metal was discussed in the first Chapter of this book, but now I will place emphasis on the physical properties of gold that make it identifiable as such. You would be utterly surprised at the number of people who will ask me, "How do you tell the difference between gold and iron pyrite — they look so much alike!" In truth, gold and iron pyrite (known commonly as "fool's gold") look absolutely *nothing* alike, and persons who say they can't tell the difference probably have never seen a piece of gold in its natural form. After you've studied the information contained in this Chapter, there will be no question in your mind as to what it is you've discovered.

The gold that is commonly found in rivers, streams, gullies and other watercourses is known as *placer* gold. (The "a" in placer is short, rhyming with "plaster.") The word placer is used to describe gold that has been eroded from its original point of occurrence (usually a quartz vein in solid, surrounding rock) and carried downhill by the forces of water and gravity until it enters the drainage system of a river or stream. Although the word "placer" is most frequently used to describe river gold that has been tumbled and shaped by the action of running water, it also can be applied to gold that has traveled a very short distance from its original outcropping.

Placer gold occurs in sizes ranging from tiny particles that can only be seen with an electron microscope, to large nuggets weighing several hundred ounces. (These are *rare,* incidentally.) Even the word "nugget" has a technical description: "A nugget is any smooth, waterworn piece of gold that weighs more than one grain." (A *grain* is a unit of measure that is used to weigh gold, and will be discussed at the end of this Chapter.)

If you have a friend who has natural, placer gold, ask him to show you his collection. Pick up one of the larger pieces and position it in the palm of one hand. Now take a piece of iron pyrite and place it in the other hand, and carry the two specimens out into the sunlight. Upon careful study of both pieces of material, you, too, will see that pyrite looks nothing like gold. In the first place, the gold will be considerably heavier — even extremely tiny pieces of gold will fall with noticeable force into the palm of your hand when dropped from a small height. Now observe the color of the specimens. The nugget of gold will look like a piece of dull, dirty, beat-up brass, while the pyrite will be bright, shiny and sparkly. Thornton's Rule Number Three: *placer gold never sparkles*!!! To illustrate this fact, turn the piece of gold around in the sunlight and notice how it always remains the same unchanging shade of yellow; it will not change color or sparkle. (One word of caution, though — never subject a gold nugget to intensive scrutiny for more than a few seconds at a time; eventually, a nugget will seem to "glow" as if some mysterious force exists inside. This is how an individual develops "gold fever," a condition that really *does* exist!)

Once you've performed the "sunlight" test on a piece of gold, try it with a hunk of pyrite. Turn the pyrite around in the sunlight and notice how its tiny cubical surfaces reflect the light of the sun in colored flashes. Sometimes pyrite will even change color as sunlight falls on its different faces. Note how the pyrite will turn, perhaps, from a bluish-green, to a yellow, to a purple, and so forth. When you see this, you'll know that you're holding a piece of the phoney stuff and that you'll have to search some more.

After studying pieces of gold and iron pyrite side by side, you should have no trouble whatsoever identifying the real thing. If for some reason you still aren't sure, there are other tests you can perform. One easy method of identifying gold is to drop the substance in question into strong, concentrated nitric acid and let it "cook." (Be extremely careful when handling nitric or any other acid, as the fumes they liberate are capable of corroding the insides of your lungs.) A piece of gold will sit in nitric acid as if it were plain water, while a piece of pyrite will smoke, crumble and disintegrate.

Another method of testing for gold is to take a small piece of the mystery substance (if you've got extras to spare) and hit it with a hammer; a piece of gold will flatten out with repeated pounding, but pyrite is brittle and will shatter into a million tiny fragments. If you should ever find a large piece of material that may be gold, whatever you do *don't* try to flatten it with a hammer; take it to an expert to obtain a positive identification. If you don't know of any gold experts in your area, you will have to try the acid test. If immersion in nitric acid has no effect on the substance, you've got yourself a prized specimen. If, however, you had flattened the piece, you'd have a large hunk of gold that *used* to be a prized specimen!

There is still another method of testing for gold, and that's to perform the "scratch test." The scratch test can yield a positive identification, but like the hammer test it is *not* for pieces that may turn out to be specimen nuggets.

Gold is a very soft metal and is given a rating of 2.5 on Moh's Scale of Hardness. (The Scale runs from one to ten, talc being the *softest* mineral substance with a hardness of one and diamond the *hardest* with a rating of ten.) To perform the scratch test, take a small piece of the material to be tested and scratch it in an inconspicuous location using the tip of a pocketknife blade. If the tip of the blade carves a scratch in the substance, you've got gold. Iron pyrite is much harder than gold and is rated approximately 6.25 on Moh's Scale; it will not be scratched by the blade.

When out panning for gold, you can easily tell when you've got the real thing in your pan. Gold is *eight times heavier* than the ordinary sand and gravel in your pan and will settle into the bottom of that utensil after a little side-sifting. (Chapter Nine of this book explains the fine art of gold panning in intricate detail.) After the panning process is completed, any gold that is present will remain mixed with the "black sands" that are always found in conjunction with placer gold. If you see specks of yellow material in the bottom of your pan, you can be fairly certain they are pieces of gold — iron pyrite of the variety found in rivers, streams, etc., is extremely light and flaky and in most cases will be washed out of your pan before you even get to the heavier materials at the bottom. If there are still doubts, try this. Slosh a surge of water over the suspected material. Notice how the black sands (which are a mixture of magnetic and non-magnetic iron ores) will wash around, while the yellow substance in the pan may or may not. If the yellow stuff *does* wash around in the bottom of the pan, you have a very peculiar type of iron pyrite that even fools the experts from time to time. However, if the yellow material seems "anchored" to the bottom of the pan and doesn't budge after subjection to the slosh treatment, you have a piece of the genuine article.

Quite frequently a prospector will encounter a heavy, silvery substance in the bottom of his pan that meets all the descriptions of gold except for its color. It is heavy, it remains fixed in the pan when sloshed, and yet what is it? It can be either one of three things. It can be platinum, lead, or else a piece of gold coated with mercury that washed down from an old tailings dump. To find out for sure, you will need to perform the acid test.

Drop the suspected material into concentrated nitric acid; the results you can expect depend upon a time factor. If the substance is a piece of gold coated with mercury, the mercury will be dissolved and assimilated into the acid; in less than five seconds you will have a piece of brilliant, yellow gold.

If the "mystery piece" remains silvery after the first few seconds of contact with nitric acid, it is not gold; you can now walk away and let the substance cook in the acid for a couple of hours. If, upon your return, the material is slowly disintegrating and giving off minute bubbles which drift to the surface of the acid, what you have is common lead which occurs in many streams of the West. Some stream lead is naturally occurring, but the vast majority comes from spent bullets, buckshot, etc., that washes into the drainage systems during periods of heavy rainfall.

If the substance in question has shown no signs of disintegration after several hours of immersion in nitric acid, there is a good chance you have a nugget of platinum. Metallic, free platinum and its sister metals — palladium, osmium, iridium, rhodium and ruthenium — occur in small quantities in several Western river systems. Some of these metals (especially iridium) are valued far in excess of gold, which is a "common metal" by comparison.

Placer gold varies in color depending upon the area in which it is found. The gold from any one particular stream will be totally unique in coloration, and the chances of gold from a different stream having the exact same color are pretty astronomical. Coloration in placer gold is caused by impurities in the metal itself. Gold that occurs in placer form is a natural alloy, sometimes containing silver, copper, iron, cadmium, platinum, and other trace elements. On the average, placer gold occurring in streams of the Western United States will run about ninety per cent gold, eight or nine per cent silver, and one or two per cent copper or platinum. The type of impurity present in gold is what determines its color. In some mining districts, placer gold is noticeably whitish, and signifies a high percentage of either silver or platinum. Reddish gold carries a substantial percentage of copper, bluish gold is mixed with a high percentage of iron, and in a small number of mining districts the gold will even be greenish! Green gold is very unusual, and is caused by a high percentage of cadmium.

Technically, the purity of gold is known as its "fineness." Fineness is based on a scale starting at zero and running up to 1,000. If someone tells you that a piece of gold is "1,000 fine," this means it is absolutely pure gold with no other material mixed in. The average nugget of placer gold will run around .900 fine, which is another way of saying it is composed of ninety per cent gold with the remainder being impurities. Based on these principles, gold that is .500 fine is fifty per cent gold, .750 fine is seventy-five per cent gold, and .250 fine would only be twenty-five per cent gold. You can also break things down into smaller terminology. For example, .990 fine would be ninety-nine per cent gold, while a bar of gold bullion stamped ".999 fine" would be 99.9 per cent pure.

A jeweler uses the "carat" system in determining the purity of gold. Absolutely pure gold is stamped "24 carat." Gold that is marked six, twelve, and eighteen carat will be twenty-five, fifty, and seventy-five per cent pure, respectively. High-quality gold jewelry is made of eighteen carat gold, the balance usually being copper or platinum.

When it finally comes time for weigh-in ceremonies, the *Troy* unit of weight is used. The Troy system of weights and measures is used solely for the purpose of weighing precious metals, the most notable being gold, silver, and platinum. Troy ounces and pounds were first used in Great Britain, and in the early 1800's the system was adapted by the United States Mint. Troy ounces and pounds differ greatly from the regular, Avoirdupois weights that are used in common, day-to-day transactions. A Troy ounce is about 1.1 times *heavier* than an Avoirdupois ounce, and therefore it will not come as a surprise when I tell you that a Troy pound only contains twelve ounces and *not* sixteen as in the Avoirdupois system. The overall Troy system of weights is made up of *four* units of measurement — grains, pennyweights (abbreviated "dwt."), ounces and pounds. To understand the system, study the following. . . .

24 grains equals 1 pennyweight (dwt.)
480 grains equals 20 pennyweights equals 1 Troy ounce
5,760 grains equals 240 pennyweights equals 12 Troy ounces equals 1 Troy pound

At this point, let me say that I am deliberately omitting tables of information that will enable you to convert Troy weight to the Avoirdupois system, and vice versa. I am doing this in order to *force you* into using the Troy system. By learning to "think Troy" from the very beginning, you will have a much easier time of things once you start getting more deeply involved — as I know you will — with the ever-fascinating world of gold.

CHAPTER SEVEN
Basic Elements of Placer Geology

Perhaps the trickiest theories yet to confront the beginning gold-dredger are those that relate to *placer geology,* also known as "the science of stream deposition." Placer geology concerns the varying conditions which cause gold and other heavy materials to be deposited in a streamflow environment. Without a doubt, the best way to learn the ins and outs of gold deposition is to place yourself at the feet of a genuine "old-timer," but unfortunately not too many of us have access to such a person; we will therefore have to study the facts relating to placer geology from books. The many types of currents, eddies, and backwashes that cause gold to be deposited in streams may seem a bit mysterious at first, but with a bit of study they will become quite clear. In fact, you'll even find yourself taking a much closer look at that river or creek you cross over every day on your way to work!

There are four principal types of placer gold deposits that will be of interest to the underwater, or for that matter, any other prospector — these are residual, eluvial, stream, and bench placers. Before we actually get into the geology of river-borne gold deposits, let's take a look at how gold finds its way into a river system. We shall start at the outcropping of a hypothetical gold vein on the wall of a river canyon and work our way downwards until we finally come to the watercourse; this process will be explained through definitions of residual and eluvial placer deposits.

The first type of placer gold deposit will occur at the surface of the ground where a gold vein crops out. This type of placer is called a *residual* deposit and is formed when the original host rock (usually quartz) erodes away, leaving pure metallic gold in place at the point of the outcrop. Gold-bearing veins located in a moist climate with heavy rainfall (southern Oregon would be an outstanding example) will erode very quickly once being exposed to the action of the surface elements, and the resulting residual placers will often extend to tens of feet in depth due to extremely deep weathering of the original vein. Such deposits were referred to as "seam diggin's" during the old days.

The next type of placer deposit is called an *eluvial* placer, and is formed after gold has traveled downward as little as a few feet from the point of its residual outcrop. (The opposite of eluvial is *alluvial*, which signifies gold that has been carried many miles from its original source.) A good example of an eluvial placer deposit would be gold that originally cropped out at the rim of a 1,000-foot-deep river canyon and has been carried by the forces of gravity and running water five hundred feet downward, with five hundred feet still remaining before it actually enters the streamflow at the bottom.

The next two types of placer deposits — bench and stream — are interrelated, and we will first discuss the deposit that will occur next along the line — this is a *stream* placer. Stream placers will be of greatest interest to the individual interested in gold-dredging, as this type of placer occurs at, near, or else under the surface of a river. There are many different types of stream placers, ranging from gravel bars just barely above the surface of the water to deeply buried bedrock deposits at the bottom of the river which generally hold more gold than the rest of the river environment.

A *bench* placer is nothing more than a stream placer that has been left high and dry by the stream that originally created it. Bench placers are created when a large land area, usually consisting of thousands of square miles, is "rejuvenated" over a period of hundreds of thousands of years and uplifted due to pressures from the earth's interior. If the land is uplifted enough, any streams in the area will start to cut downward until they reach their new "base level," which will be that of sea level. As a river cuts downward over a long enough period of time, the bed it originally occupied before the uplift will be left stranded above the new stream level. Bench placers (also known as "terrace" deposits) are often very rich in gold, only these gravels are out of reach as far as the gold-dredger is concerned. (See Figure 17, which illustrates the "basic four" placer deposits.)

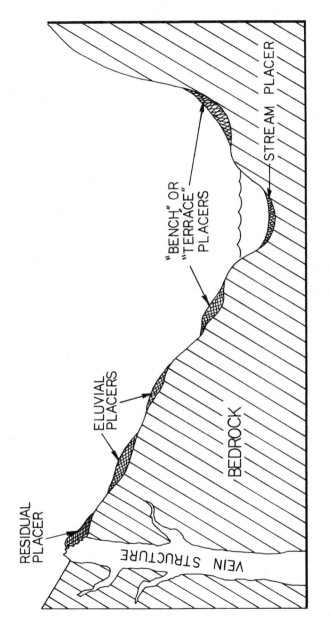

Figure 17—The "basic four" types of placer deposits.

85

The factors governing the occurrence of placer gold in a river environment are many, and quite often complex. There are so many variables involved in the science of placer geology it would be virtually impossible to mention all of them, but basically, the deposition of heavy materials in a stream is based upon the speed and volume of water flow coupled with the shape and slope of the river channel. Throw in obstructions such as large boulders, bedrock outcroppings, etc., and you have a whole *new* ball game.

Gold is transported in a stream principally during periods of high water, such as during the yearly spring runoff. Because gold is heavy and tends to settle in cracks and crevices at the bottom of a river, the speed of a runoff current has to be very great in order for transportation to occur. An ideal situation for heavy flooding and runoff would be as follows. . . .

The mountains in the high country where "River X" is born are covered with one to two feet of snow, and a warm, rain-bearing storm moves in. Heavy rain starts to fall — one inch, two inches, five, ten — and in a matter of hours River X starts to rise from its banks with extreme rapidity. But River X is not merely rising from the heavy rains — the warm rains, as they fall on the shallow snowpack, turn that snow into water which also goes into the river. (It is a known fact that heavy rains falling on a shallow snowpack will melt it rapidly, whereas a deeper layer of snow will often absorb large amounts of rainfall.)

It has been twelve hours since the storm front moved in, and River X is raging like the mighty Mississippi during one of her frequent fits of rage. If you could observe River X at this time, you could study *firsthand* the conditions that lead to the deposition of placer gold. You would see a river that is flowing a filthy, muddy brown from tons of suspended silt. You would see branches, twigs, and even entire trees floating downstream with the swift current. If you dared to stick your head beneath the surface (as if you could even view anything, with all that muddy water), you would "see" small boulders bouncing along the bottom of the river as if they were mere pebbles. But if you knew what to look for, you would notice other things as well. For example, in the midst of the mighty turbulence you might see areas where the swift currents give way to quiet pools. Perhaps you would see large sections of bedrock projecting into the turbulence, causing the current to swirl around in an "eddy" motion. Or what about that monstrous, twenty-foot-wide boulder out in the middle of the stream — is it your imagination, or is the current really "standing still" on its downstream side?

"River X," as I'm sure you realize, is hypothetical, yet the three streamflow characteristics just mentioned are *real* and may be encountered in any river or creek. These three conditions are variations of the two basic principles of placer geology: (1) Gold and other heavy materials will settle wherever a stream current slows down and drops its load, or (2) wherever heavy materials encounter an obstruction which causes them to "hang up."

One of the big factors affecting the speed of a stream current — and thereby the deposition of gold — is the degree of slope of the stream's channel. The slope of a stream channel (known commonly as "gradient") may range from extremely steep to almost flat. In general, the closer you are to the headwaters of a stream the steeper the gradient will be. A steeply sloping channel will cause a river to flow very swiftly, usually causing gold to be carried along with little deposition. There are exceptions, of course. If there are major obstructions on the bottom of the stream channel, gold will be trapped no matter how steep the gradient (or swift the current).

As a stream leaves its headwaters and approaches its middle range, the gradient of the channel will decrease. As the slope of a stream channel decreases the current will run considerably slower, creating conditions more favorable for the deposition of heavy materials. The slope of the channel in the headwater area may have been as great as a couple of hundred feet per mile, but it will now average around thirty or forty feet per mile. The former figure seems to be the ideal gradient for the deposition of placer gold.

The speed of the current and gradient of the stream channel also have a great deal to do with the amount of unwanted overburden that will be deposited in a river. There are variables, but for the most part a steep gradient (coupled with a swift current such as that found near the headwaters) will result in the deposition of relatively little overburden. The further downstream you go the gentler the gradient will become, causing slower currents and the deposition of more overburden. (The middle ranges of a river are the most popular with gold-dredgers, as the depth of the overburden rarely exceeds twenty feet.) If you venture *further* downstream toward the mouth of a river, the gradient becomes even gentler, and sometimes approaches a level plane. An example of this would be the point where a river empties into a large valley upon its emergence from mountainous terrain. The overburden at the mouth of a river often will be hundreds of feet in depth, completely beyond the reach of conventional suction dredges.

As stated in previous chapters, gold is an extremely heavy metal, and when it enters a river channel, it will travel very grudgingly. Larger and heavier pieces of gold will always travel the path of *least resistance* in their journey downstream. Let us study this curious phenomenon as it is portrayed in Figure 18.

Let us assume that a very rich gold vein is cropping out on the side of a hill above the small gulley shown in the upper left portion of Figure 18. As the gold vein is eroded by the elements, the gold will

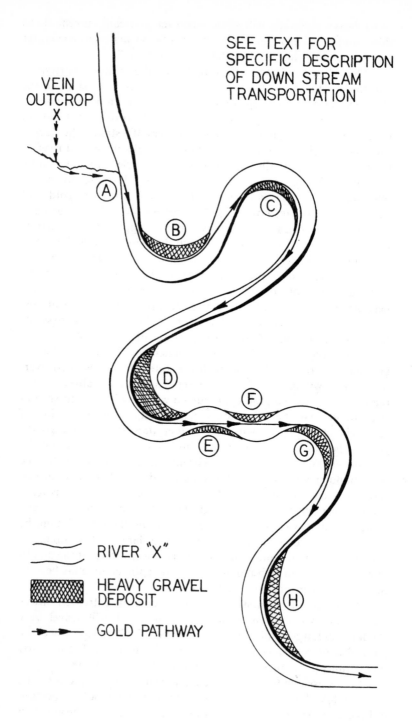

Figure 18—The transportation of gold down "River X."

be released from its quartz matrix and travel down the hill and enter the gulley; the gulley eventually pours its golden treasure into the drainage of River X.

The gold in our small gulley enters River X at *Point A*, and will rest at that location until some time in the future when a major flood creates enough current to lift the gold from its resting place and start the downstream transportation process. When such a swift water period occurs, the gold will move from Point A across the river to the sharp inside bend at *Point B*. The transportation of gold in a river is simple to understand if you'll just remember this one basic fact — "Because of its weight, gold will travel downstream in a straight line following the shortest possible path *from inside bend to inside bend.*" But back, now, to Figure 18.

At Point B you will notice there is a shaded area at the inside tip of the bend. This is a gravel bar, and it was formed at this location because the current of the stream slowed down when it rounded the inside bend of the curve. Whenever a stream current slows down, the river loses its power to transport the material it is carrying in suspension at times of flooding. In the case of the sharp inside bend at Point B, the current would slow considerably, causing larger boulders and heavy gravel components to drop almost immediately; one of those heavy gravel components would be *gold.*

After rounding the inside of the bend at Point B, our hypothetical gold nuggets would shoot across River X to the head of the next large gravel bar at *Point C*. Point C is actually a long, arc-like curve with a gentle inside bend, and in a case such as this the gold and other heavy materials would be deposited along the entire length of the curve.

After leaving Point C our nuggets will again shoot across the river, this time over to *Point D*. Upon traveling around this bend our gold encounters a series of curves whose inside bends form an exact straight line. In a case such as this, gold will travel the line between inside bends as if someone got out and marked a pathway with a straightedge. Our nuggets will touch Points *E, F,* and *G* and then swing around the latter bend and over to *Point H* where they will again accumulate; from here, they leave the scene once and for all. Study this illustration well, friends, particularly the inside bends where deposits of heavy gravel material are indicated. Even though "River X" is purely fictitious, the depositional spots portrayed here are one hundred per cent *genuine!*

At this time I'd like to point out that gravel bars at the tips of inside bends aren't the only places for gold to be deposited. Placer gold and heavy stream gravels will accumulate *any place* where a stream current slackens. Examples would be the tail end of rapids where currents change from swift to placid, the upper end of deep pools which often act as "gravel dumps," and places in a river canyon where the channel widens out upon emergence from a "narrows." When you finally get around to visiting a genuine mountain gold stream, you'll undoubtedly spot many more depositionary areas yourself. The practice will do you good!

To search for dredging locations in areas where heavy stream materials have been deposited may sound like fun and games, but if you expect to find enough gold to make your mining efforts worthwhile, you will have to do much more than make a casual surveillance. Just because you've found a nice, wide gravel bar or a deep, still pool doesn't mean you'll hit the proverbial jackpot. The gold you can expect to recover will depend upon the *nature of the bedrock* at the bottom of the deposit. I briefly touched upon the subject of bedrock in an earlier chapter, but it is now time to elaborate.

As placer gold is being carried downstream by the action of currents, the pieces of any substantial weight will gradually work their way downward through the overburden until they reach bedrock, which forms a solid, usually impenetrable obstacle to their further downward progress. Notice how I use the word *usually*. Bedrock will act as an absolute base-level for gold's downward motion if it is smooth and uniform, but smooth bedrock will frequently give way to stretches containing crevices extending down into the rock "basement." Heavy pieces of gold moving downward through the overburden will find their way into these crevices, and again start their downward movement until they have reached the absolute bottom. Here they will stay, sometimes for thousands of years, unless a dredger with the proper knowledge comes along to recover them. (Figure 19) If the idea of a piece of gold staying in one crevice for thousands of years sounds somewhat "final," that's because *it is.* Once a heavy gold nugget gets lodged tightly in the bottom of a bedrock crevice, it will take a magnitude "ten" earthquake to uplift the bedrock enough so that the stream current can completely wash away the overburden and eventually wear away at the bare bedrock itself, thereby releasing the gold.

After you have located a section of river where heavy materials have been deposited, you should make a careful inspection of any visible bedrock for evidence of crevice structure. In general, bedrocks composed of slate-phyllite are most apt to develop crevices because of their "cleavage planes." In the case of slate-phyllite, cleavage is best defined as the tendency of a rock to break off into "sheets." When slate-phyllite forms the bedrock of a river, it will frequently break off along its cleavage planes upon subjection to pounding from large boulders during times of flooding. When pieces of slate-phyllite bedrock break off, crevices that trap gold will remain between the sheets that still protrude. (Figure 20)

PLACER GOLD WILL ALWAYS
WORK ITS WAY TO THE
ABSOLUTE <u>BOTTOM</u> OF A
BEDROCK CREVICE

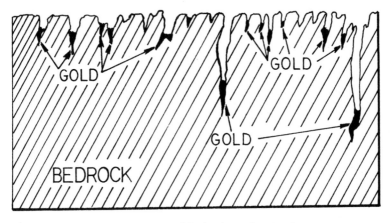

Figure 19—Diagram of bedrock crevice structure.

SLATE-PHYLLITE BEDROCK, BECAUSE OF
ITS TENDENCY TO "CLEAVE," IS NOTORIOUS
FOR ITS ABILITY TO TRAP GOLD. (SEE TEXT)

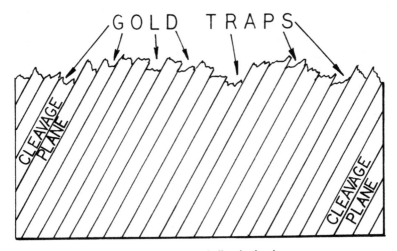

Figure 20—Slate-phyllite bedrock.

Under certain conditions granite will act as a favorable bedrock, but all too often this very resistant rock will develop a "tabletop" polish that will allow even the heaviest of gold nuggets to wash right on over. If you desire to prospect in a granite area, look for "joints" where large blocks of this material come together; there will often be crevices at such points. (Figure 21)

Another type of crevice that is particularly excellent for trapping gold is that which occurs whenever a bedrock quartz vein erodes, leaving a jagged depression in the bedrock surface. (Figure 22) Bedrock quartz veins are often gold-bearing, and are the source for many gold-quartz nuggets still found in Western rivers to this date. This is a prize worth searching for!

A gold-diver will often become excited upon discovery of a deep pothole in the bedrock of a river, but nine times out of ten these "glory holes" will turn out to be a complete *bust*. Potholes are formed when complex currents cause heavy gravels and small boulders to spin around in eddy-like motions, scouring deep holes in the bedrock. If a piece of gold falls into such a pothole (often referred to as a "boil hole"), it will most likely be ground up by the eddy action of the gravels. The fine, powdery gold that may once have been a beautiful specimen nugget *before* entering the pothole will now wash out with the current and continue its journey downstream. (Figure 23-A)

But there are exceptions to every rule. If you should ever locate a pothole filled with large, coarse gravels packed in hard like cement, run — don't walk — to the nearest available gold dredge! You just might be onto one of those rare gold traps that was accidentally passed up by the original Gold Rushers back in the 1850's. Potholes of this nature have yielded pounds of gold, particularly if they occur in jagged, pockety bedrock. (Figure 23-B)

So far I've talked of crevices and potholes that extend down into the bedrock, but there are also gold traps that *protrude* from the bedrock surface. A good example of this would be a "dike" of hard, resistant rock material that originally intruded its way up into softer, surrounding rock that eventually became the bottom of a river canyon. Over a period of thousands of years, the pounding of boulders on the bottom of the stream channel wore away much of the soft country rock leaving the harder dikes protruding from the bedrock. (See figures 24-A and B.) If the dike has a good slant against the direction of the stream current, heavy materials will catch under the resulting overhang on the upstream side of the dike (24-A); when the dike slants downstream, the resulting overhang will often act as a natural riffle and cause an eddy current to form. The eddy action will tend to concentrate heavy materials under the downstream side of the overhang (24-B).

GRANITE IS A VERY RESISTANT ROCK THAT ALL TOO OFTEN DEVELOPS A "TABLE-TOP POLISH"; STILL, CREVICES WILL FORM AT "JOINTS" WHERE BLOCKS OF GRANITE COME TOGETHER.

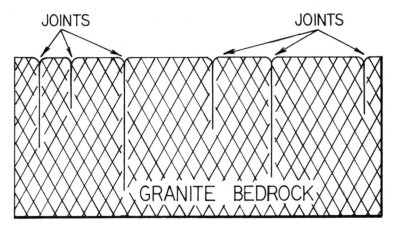

Figure 21—Where to find crevices in granite bedrock.

A DECOMPOSING QUARTZ VEIN AT THE BOTTOM OF A RIVER — GOLD-BEARING OR NOT — WILL LEAVE A JAGGED DEPRESSION IN THE BEDROCK, FORMING AN OUTSTANDING **GOLD TRAP.**

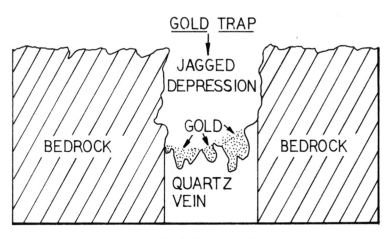

Figure 22—Bedrock "quartz vein" crevice.

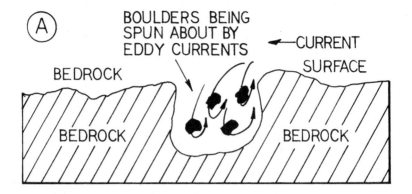

THIS IS THE TYPE OF POTHOLE YOU SHOULD AVOID; THE EDDY ACTION OF THE CHURNING ROCKS AND GRAVELS WILL GRIND GOLD NUGGETS DOWN TO POWDER, FLUSHING THE RESULTING "FLOUR" GOLD BACK INTO THE FLOW OF THE STREAM CURRENT.

★　　★　　★

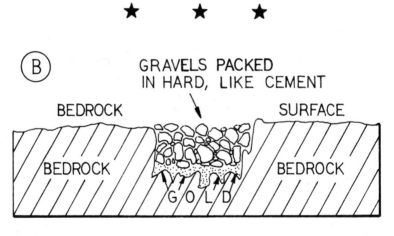

THIS IS THE TYPE OF POTHOLE IN WHICH YOU **MAY** JUST FIND SOMETHING WORTHWHILE. IF YOU EVER COME ACROSS A POTHOLE FILLED WITH HARD-PACKED GRAVELS (ESPECIALLY IN AN AREA WITH JAGGED BED-ROCK), CLEAN IT TO THE VERY BOTTOM . . . YOU MAY VERY WELL FIND A "BONANZA!"

Figure 23—Diagrams of bedrock "potholes."

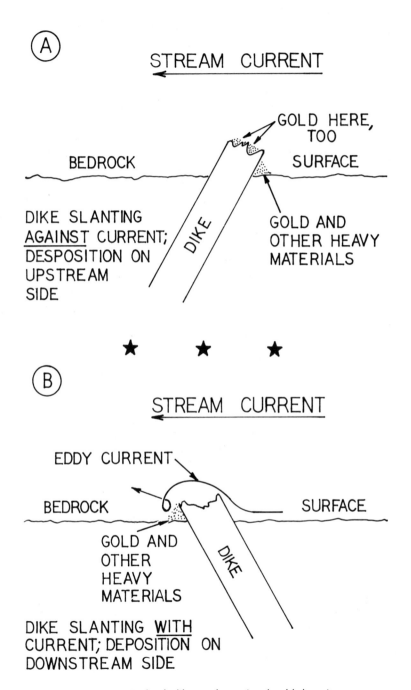

Figure 24—Bedrock dikes and associated gold deposits.

The crevice systems in a bedrock are most apt to catch and hold placer gold when they cut at angles perpendicular to the flow of the stream. (Figure 25) The closer the angle approaches ninety degrees, the better. If you can locate slate-phyllite bedrock, for example, with cleavage planes that slant *against* the flow of the current while cutting the stream at ninety degrees, you have located the "gold-divers' dream." But at the same time don't overlook long, narrow crevices that run parallel with the streamflow — they, too, can hold bonanzas. The width of parallel crevices will usually vary, going from narrow to wide, wide to narrow, etc. The point where the crevice narrows down from a wide portion is an exceedingly good gold trap that is often overlooked by the uninitiated. The same will hold true for crevices that wander across the bedrock at irregular angles, such as forty-five degrees. (Figure 26)

It is a common misconception among beginning gold-dredgers that if they vacuum their way down to bedrock and lay it bare, they can pick up the nuggets with their fingers. Unfortunately, this is not the case. True, there will often be small flakes of gold occurring on the bedrock surface, but larger nuggets will almost always be lodged tightly into the crevice structure. The only way of recovering *all* the gold from a given section of bedrock is to pry the crevices open and scrape them clean. (The recovery of gold from an underwater crevice is a *fine art*, and there is actually much more to it than I've mentioned here; complete details will be found in Chapter Eight.)

CREVICES THAT CUT THE
BEDROCK OF A STREAM AT
ANGLES **PERPENDICULAR**
TO THE FLOW ARE APT TO BE
THE BEST GOLD TRAPS.

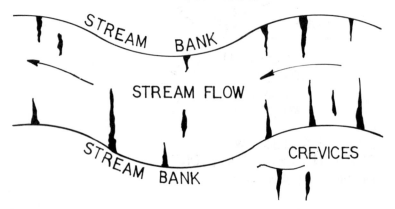

Figure 25—Diagram of crevices cutting streambed at perpendicular angles.

DON'T OVERLOOK THE CREVICE THAT PARALLELS THE STREAM FLOW... IT TOO CAN HOLD GOLD, ESPECIALLY AT POINTS WHERE IT NARROWS, BENDS, OR HAS BEEN BLOCKED BY AN OBSTRUCTION.

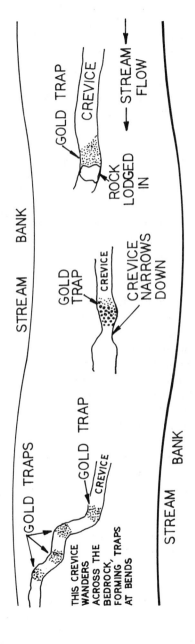

STREAM BANK

GOLD TRAPS

GOLD TRAP

CREVICE

THIS CREVICE WANDERS ACROSS THE BEDROCK, FORMING TRAPS AT BENDS

GOLD TRAP

CREVICE

CREVICE NARROWS DOWN

GOLD TRAP

CREVICE

ROCK LODGED IN

STREAM FLOW

STREAM BANK

Figure 26—Diagram of parallel crevice structure.

Rivers that flow through mountainous terrain rarely, if ever, have a free and easy pathway to follow on their long and eventual journey to a valley or sea. From start to finish, the channel of a mountain stream will resist the smooth flow of water by presenting one obstacle after another. An on-the-spot inspection of a mountain river will reveal such features as monstrous boulders, sections of bedrock jutting into the stream as if to choke off its life flow, perhaps even waterfalls that plunge dozens of feet to dark, mysterious pools below. In spite of its chaotic appearance, everything is in perfect order in a mountain streamflow environment, and we will have to study it for what it is — obstructions and all.

The most common obstruction to prevent the smooth flow of water in a mountainous river channel is the common *boulder.* Boulders come in all shapes and sizes, ranging from minor nuisances a foot or two across all the way up to gigantic masses of rock the size of a bungalow. Boulders that fall between these two extremes deserve the attention of the underwater prospector, because they will often concentrate huge amounts of gold near their bases — particularly if they rest on bedrock.

Strange things happen when the gold-carrying flood current of a river encounters a large boulder. Let's study Figure 27 to get the story. In this hypothetical situation we have a large, somewhat rounded boulder in the middle of a stream that is at the height of its yearly flood stage. The current is flowing at a frightening clip, and we surely wouldn't want to fall in at this time! As the swift current slams into the upstream side of the boulder, it is deflected around the outside perimeter due to the roundness of the rock mass. When the current "rounds the corner" and approaches the downstream side of the boulder, it will start to circulate in an eddy motion around the rear of the boulder and practically stand still. If the stream current happens to be transporting gold, the heavy yellow metal will be carried along the perimeter of the boulder to eventually settle in the still waters on the *downstream side.* It is possible for gold to be trapped on the upstream side of a boulder, but usually there will have to be a substantial fissure in the face of the rock mass to catch the gold as it is impaled against the boulder by the current.

Boulders often have yielded large amounts of gold to the dredger who diligently cleans them down to the base, but which boulders, specifically, are most apt to hold the golden treasure? The answer is simple — look for large boulders in mid-stream that obstruct the flow of current as it travels from inside bend to inside bend. (Figure 28) As we already know, gold tends to travel from the tip of one inside bend to the other, but if there is an obstruction in the current flow as it shoots between bends (namely a boulder), some of the heavier gold will never make it to the inside of the next bend. Always keep an eye out for this type of condition, and check the downstream side of any large boulders that appear to be in the correct position. And, of course, don't overlook large boulders deeply imbedded in gravel bars — coarse gold just loves to "hang up" in such a spot!

One of the best of all possible spots for the deposition of placer gold will be around an accumulation of large boulders at a point where a stream channel widens. (Figure 29) In the upper part of Figure 29, the river is traveling through an extremely narrow gap, a channel condition which causes currents to flow at tremendous speeds. The water is so swift it even carries large boulders which don't get a chance to settle in the narrows. As soon as the stream emerges from the narrows, the large boulders will drop immediately at the beginning of the widening. If you really want to find a potential "super-spot," check the gravel on the downstream sides of boulders such as this.

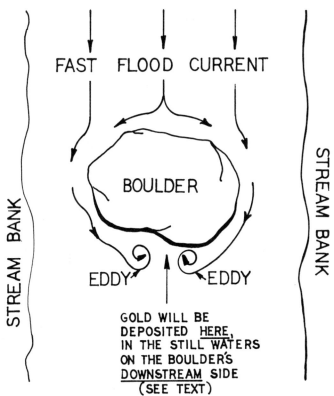

Figure 27—The deposition of gold around a boulder.

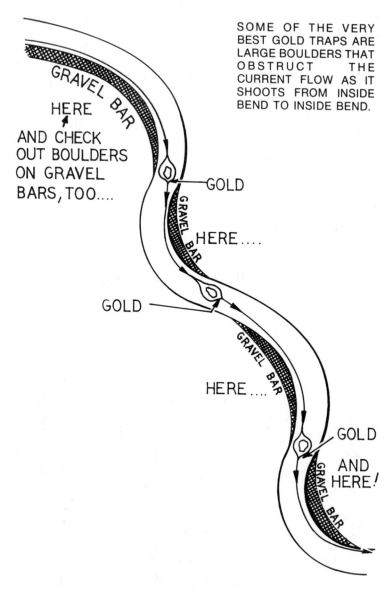

SOME OF THE VERY BEST GOLD TRAPS ARE LARGE BOULDERS THAT OBSTRUCT THE CURRENT FLOW AS IT SHOOTS FROM INSIDE BEND TO INSIDE BEND.

GRAVEL BAR

HERE

AND CHECK OUT BOULDERS ON GRAVEL BARS, TOO....

GOLD

GRAVEL BAR

HERE....

GOLD

GRAVEL BAR

HERE....

GOLD

AND HERE!

GRAVEL BAR

Figure 28—Boulder obstructions between inside bends.

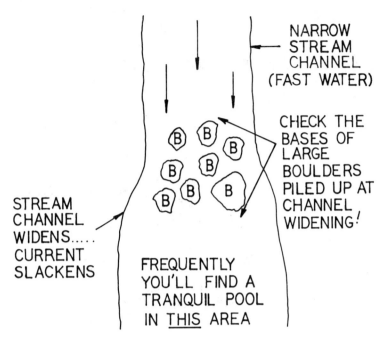

NARROW STREAM CHANNEL (FAST WATER)

CHECK THE BASES OF LARGE BOULDERS PILED UP AT CHANNEL WIDENING!

STREAM CHANNEL WIDENS..... CURRENT SLACKENS

FREQUENTLY YOU'LL FIND A TRANQUIL POOL IN THIS AREA

Figure 29—Boulder accumulation at stream channel widening.

Boulders are not the only objects to obstruct stream channels to the advantage of the gold-dredger. Another very favorable location will be an area where a large section of bedrock protrudes out into a stream, causing an eddy current to circulate around the outcropping. Whenever a chunk of bedrock sticks out into a river on an angle slanting *with* the current, an eddy will circulate on the downstream side of the obstruction causing a buildup of heavy material. This type of eddy is called a *suction eddy*. (Figure 30-A) If the current flowing across the face of a downstream-slanted bedrock outcrop is fierce enough, it will sometimes shoot across the stream and cause an eddy to circulate around an object on the opposite bank; this condition is known as a *pressure eddy*. (Figure 30-B)

The nature of bedrock outcroppings that protrude into a stream channel *against* the flow of the current is tricky, and one would almost have to see the river in question at the height of its flood stage to get an idea of where the eddy currents will form. An outcropping that protrudes far out into the current (as shown in Figure 31-A) will most likely catch the current on the outermost projection of the bedrock and cause an eddy to swirl in toward the shore. The spot indicated by the "X" would be a possible depositionary area. If the outcropping is only a minor projection into the flow of the current (Figure 31-B), any number of things can

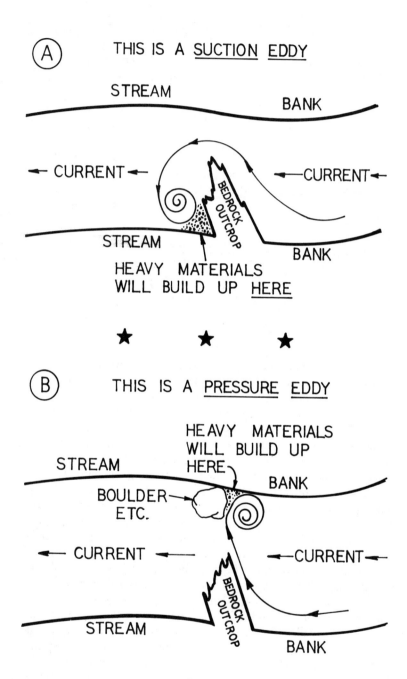

Figure 30—Diagrams of suction and pressure eddies.

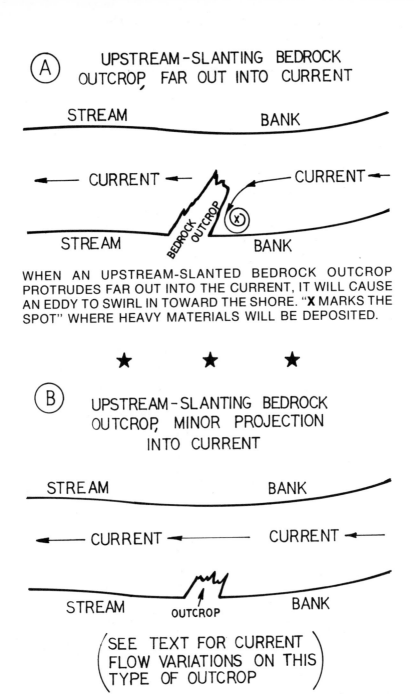

A UPSTREAM-SLANTING BEDROCK OUTCROP, FAR OUT INTO CURRENT

STREAM   BANK

◄— CURRENT ◄—   — CURRENT ◄—

STREAM   BEDROCK OUTCROP   BANK

WHEN AN UPSTREAM-SLANTED BEDROCK OUTCROP PROTRUDES FAR OUT INTO THE CURRENT, IT WILL CAUSE AN EDDY TO SWIRL IN TOWARD THE SHORE. "**X** MARKS THE SPOT" WHERE HEAVY MATERIALS WILL BE DEPOSITED.

★　　★　　★

B UPSTREAM-SLANTING BEDROCK OUTCROP, MINOR PROJECTION INTO CURRENT

STREAM   BANK

◄— CURRENT ◄—   — CURRENT ◄—

STREAM   OUTCROP   BANK

(SEE TEXT FOR CURRENT FLOW VARIATIONS ON THIS TYPE OF OUTCROP)

Figure 31—Bedrock outcroppings slanting against current.

happen. The stream current can bypass the projection entirely, it can partially flow against the outcrop with the major part running out toward the middle of the channel, or the major portion can flow against the outcrop and circulate in a "half eddy," flushing the material in suspension back out into the middle of the stream. Now you can understand why I say an on-the-spot inspection of an upstream-slanted bedrock outcropping is a virtual necessity!

Every so often you will hear stories about how a gold-dredger recovered a fabulous amount of gold from the base of a waterfall. Before *you* start getting "waterfall happy," let's set the record straight once and for all.

The average waterfall — if it is of any substantial height — creates downward currents of extreme ferocity and will tend to carve a deep, turbulent boil hole right at its base. (See Figure 32) Nine times out of ten, any gold coming over the falls will drop into this boil hole to be ground up into flakes that will soon wash out with the current. So in this sense, anyway, waterfalls should be avoided when you're out looking for dredging spots.

But as we have seen many times during the course of this text, there *are* exceptions to every rule, and in this case the exception is a humdinger. Every so often a waterfall will flow over a layer of extremely hard, weather-resistant rock that overlays softer rock beneath. As water goes over the falls, it will cause the underlying

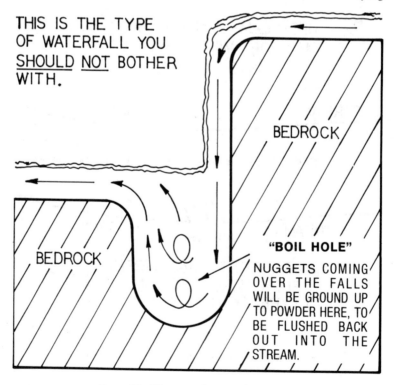

THIS IS THE TYPE OF WATERFALL YOU SHOULD NOT BOTHER WITH.

BEDROCK

BEDROCK

"BOIL HOLE"

NUGGETS COMING OVER THE FALLS WILL BE GROUND UP TO POWDER HERE, TO BE FLUSHED BACK OUT INTO THE STREAM.

Figure 32—Diagram of a typical waterfall.

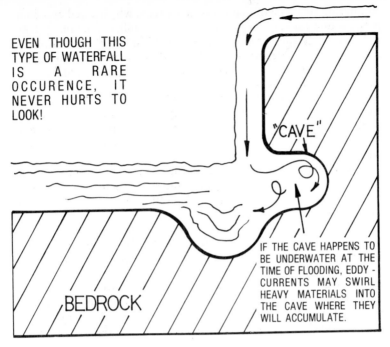

EVEN THOUGH THIS TYPE OF WATERFALL IS A RARE OCCURENCE, IT NEVER HURTS TO LOOK!

"CAVE"

BEDROCK

IF THE CAVE HAPPENS TO BE UNDERWATER AT THE TIME OF FLOODING, EDDY - CURRENTS MAY SWIRL HEAVY MATERIALS INTO THE CAVE WHERE THEY WILL ACCUMULATE.

Figure 33—Waterfall with an underlying "cave."

softer rock to erode back under the upper layer of harder material. This will create a kind of "cave" under the falls. (Figure 33) If the cave happens to be below the water line at the time of flooding, a powerful eddy current may develop which will occasionally (and I do emphasize the word *occasionally*) cause heavy materials to swirl back into the cave and become entrapped. There have been a number of fabulously rich dredging finds taken from such locations, but you could count the grand total on the fingers of one hand. Even so, it will pay you to take no chances . . . investigate!

Thus far in our discussion, we have covered many, many types of conditions which are favorable for the deposition of placer gold. At this point, I think you are ready to be exposed to some of the most important material any gold-dredger could ever read: "The Sequence of Tailings Principle." What's that? You say you've never heard of it? That's probably because nobody has ever given this material a name until now, and the very tiny number of mining people who *do* know about it would probably want it kept under lock and key. Well, I don't care about all of that nonsense . . . right now I'm going to share it with *all of you*.

Earlier in this Chapter, I discussed how placer gold is very heavy, and how it will eventually work its way down toward the bedrock of a stream. Now, this is a long-standing, undisputed principle of placer geology, and many gold-dredgers have the nuggets to prove it. However, there is also a time when placer gold can be found *right on the surface* of a river gravel deposit, with the bedrock down below being *absolutely barren!* Your best chance of en-

105

countering this type of deposit is in a stream which acted as a dumping ground for very large amounts of hydraulic mine tailings from rich "gravel terrace" deposits up on the hillsides. The deposition of tailings into the stream would have begun some time during the mid-1850's, shortly after its waters had been diverted and the bedrock laid bare to strip it of its gold values.

After hydraulic miners processed the large quantities of extremely low-grade gravel from the uppermost level of the terrace deposit, the tailings from these gravels (also extremely low-grade) flowed into the river down below and settled out on the bedrock which had just recently been laid bare.

Next, the intermediate level of the terrace was worked, and the tailings from these gravels (a little bit richer than the uppermost level) flowed into the river and settled out into a layer on top of the one already covering the bedrock.

Finally, the exceptionally rich bedrock level of the gravel terrace was mined. The tailings from this level (which naturally contained more gold inasmuch as the original gravels themselves were so rich) now flowed into the river and settled out *on top* of the two initial layers of lower-grade tailings. What we have here is a classic case of *reverse deposition*. The original levels of gravel in the terrace deposit were richest from bottom to top; the *tailings* from these terrace gravels, now found in the river below, are richest from *top to bottom*.

What does all of this mean to a gold-dredger? Simply this: any time you are dredging an area where the gold is very plentiful on the surface, but starts getting leaner and leaner as you work your way down, it may be to your advantage to keep on working the surface layers *only* and FORGET ABOUT GOING ANY DEEPER. Chances are, you are working a gravel deposit made up of old terrace tailings; by going deeper, you will run into all of the extremely low-grade tailings that were deposited in the river before the richer tailings came along. NOTE — In certain sections of the country (namely, Northern California) you might also encounter the hydraulic tailings from ancient Tertiary channel deposits located high up on the ridge tops. The "Sequence of Tailings Principle" also applies to this type of deposit.

At this point there is probably a nagging question in the back of your mind: "Just when *should* I bother going all the way down to bedrock to see what's there?" The answer is, always punch at least one quick "sample" hole down to bedrock, even if it appears that most of your gold is coming from the surface. There is always the chance you are working a spot where the river was never diverted to strip the bedrock of its gold, in which case there will be a layer of coarse, poorly sorted rocks and boulders *in between* the bottommost layer of low-grade tailings and the bedrock. Now, such a layer of rocks and boulders does not absolutely guarantee the bedrock below will be virgin; the bedrock still may have been stripped, and the rocky layer washed onto it before the first low-grade hydraulic tailings came along. In conclusion, there is only one way to be *totally* sure about the spot you are working: punch that sample hole all the way down to bedrock!

CHAPTER EIGHT

Sniping, Sampling, and Sizing up a Gold Placer

Long before a gold-diver carries his "heavy artillery" (namely a dredge) into an area, he will perform extensive tests to see if a hot spot is really as "hot" as it initially appears; this is known as *sampling*. Sampling is done with an absolute minimum of lightweight equipment, and an experienced prospector can cover a mile or more of river a day checking areas that show overt indications of gold. Once he has located potential "drop-spots," he will sample the more easily accessible gold traps of the area to test their values.

There are two basic methods of sampling a stream. You can look for traces of gold *above* the water line by sinking test holes into gravel bars, cleaning out cracks in exposed surface bedrock, and panning the roots of plants and weeds growing at water's edge (roots are great for catching smaller pieces of gold when they're underwater at flood stage; they act like "tentacles"). But to tell the honest truth, you'll be much better off in the long run if you learn and master the *professional* method of sampling — the pros call it "sniping," or "crevicing." Sniping (or crevicing, whichever you prefer) involves the underwater inspection of gold traps by the use of diving suit, face mask, snorkel, and simple hand tools. You don't have to be a master of underwater diving techniques to snipe, but you will need a little knowledge of some of the basic equipment that is necessary.

A major obstacle confronting all snipers in mountain gold streams is cold water. Depending upon the time of year, water temperatures can vary anywhere from the low thirties to the upper seventies. It is difficult for a person to endure water colder than normal body temperature for any great length of time, and some type of protective diving suit is a necessity. There are many styles of diving suits manufactured today, but all of them fall into one of two categories — they are either "wet" suits or "dry" suits.

The dry diving suit was the first protective "exposure" suit to be introduced, and has actually been around since the late 1800's. In fact, it is the "sub-aqueous armour" that was described back in Chapter Two. Today's dry suits, of course, are considerably better than the original gear, but there are enough similarities to make the two suits appear practically the same.

A dry suit is made of thin sheet rubber, and is loose-fitting except at the ankles, wrists, and neck where it must fit tightly to keep out the water. It is common for a diver to wear "longjohn" woolen underwear under a dry suit for thermal insulation; while this suit does do a good job of keeping out water, the thin rubber doesn't do much to keep out the *cold.* The conventional dry diving suit is not very popular among gold-divers because it is very easy for the sheet rubber to tear on rocks and other underwater objects. Also, the water pressure encountered at deeper-than-normal depths compresses the folds and wrinkles in the rubber against the diver's skin, leading to considerable discomfort.

The most advanced type of dry diving suit manufactured today is constructed of neoprene rubber. In use, it is partially inflated with air to form a positive, virtually water-tight "buffer zone" between the suit and the diver's skin. This type of dry suit is custom-tailored for the individual who will be wearing it, and is for the diver who needs the utmost in protection against the effects of cold water. Despite the price tag which frequently runs as high as $350, gold-divers will immediately fall in love with this suit the first time they see one hanging from the rack at their local dive shop.

The wet diving suit is the type used by the vast majority of divers today, including those who dive for reasons other than gold recovery. The wet suit is made of neoprene rubber, and comes in varying thicknesses. A wet suit is tight-fitting (like the inflatable dry suit, it is frequently custom-tailored to an individual's measurements) and fits like a "second skin." Water from the outside will slowly seep through the neoprene and become entrapped between the suit and the diver's skin. After a few minutes of physical exertion, the diver's body temperature will heat this trapped water, forming a warm, insulating layer that allows the diver to work comfortably for several hours. A diver intending to snipe (and eventually dredge) in cold mountain rivers will usually choose a quarter-inch thick "Farmer John" wet suit, together with neoprene hood, booties, and gloves to round out the package. The price of a good quarter-inch Farmer John wet suit will start out in the $150-$175 range.

Before we delve into the actual principles of sniping and sampling, let's familiarize ourselves with the basic "hand" accessories of the gold-divers' profession. Referring to Figure 34, we can see that there are nine pieces of equipment that make up the sniper's tool kit. They are face mask, snorkel, a sturdy all-metal rock hammer, an "I-beam" pry bar, crevicing tool, suction-gun, a long pair of tweezers, a sample bottle for holding gold finds, and a gold pan. (Mask and snorkel are considered accessories because they can be used with or without a full diving suit.) As we study the various steps employed in sniping, I'll discuss these implements in the order in which they are commonly used.

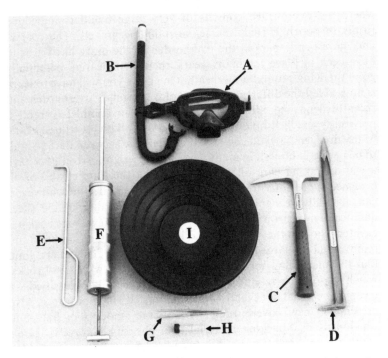

Figure 34—Here you can see the various pieces of equipment that make up the "sniper's tool kit." The kit consists of face mask (A), snorkel (B), rock hammer (C), I-beam pry bar (D), crevicing tool (E), suction-gun (F), tweezers (G), sample bottle (H), and gold pan (I). These "hand" utensils are commonly used for sampling crevices prior to carrying in a suction dredge. (For specific information on how to use each piece of equipment, see text.)

After you've located an area where heavy materials have been deposited, you will need to don your wet (or dry) suit and make a careful underwater inspection of the bedrock. Break out your *face mask* and *snorkel,* attach the snorkel tube to the headband of your mask, and adjust the latter to the correct size; you're now ready to dive in and make your preliminary investigation.

A free diver wearing only wet suit, face mask, and snorkel will tend to be buoyant and float in the water, and you can take advantage of this by employing simple hand motion to propel yourself across the stream while keeping your face under the surface, inspecting the bottom. As you scan the bottom of the stream, make mental note of the following conditions: Is the bedrock as smooth as a tabletop, or pockety and full of crevices? If crevices are present, do they cut across the stream at a nice, perpendicular angle? If they run parallel with the current, are there any narrow points that will act as gold traps?

When making an initial underwater surveillance, it is a good idea to inspect the overburden itself. Keep an eye out for areas where the overburden consists of very large boulders imbedded firmly in poorly sorted, coarse, surrounding gravels. The coarser and more firmly packed the overburden is, the more likely it is to have been in place for many years, thereby indicating potentially good dredging ground underneath. One thing you will have to learn is how to tell the difference between old, "original" overburden and recently deposited "flood gravel" which can completely refill a previously dredged hole in a time span of only two or three years. Many dredgers say you *can't tell* the difference between the two and, to be perfectly honest, in many cases they are right; a river *does* have a way of taking care of itself, by "wiping the slate clean" of all evidence of previous dredging. A really experienced sniper, however, can generally recognize "new" overburden because of the sheer absence of monstrous boulders. If a dredger of a few years back excavated a hole in the overburden at the location you're sampling and removed all the large boulders from the area, the chances are good that the succeeding spring runoffs filled the hole with small rocks, which very much resemble "classified" gravels. By "classified," I mean gravels that are evenly sized and "sorted" in appearance. Also present in "new" overburden will be large amounts of fine sand which acts as "packing material" for the small gravels. Here's another way to tell if a spot has been dredged previously (provided there hasn't been a "killer flood" in the intervening years, which will have wiped away all evidence). If, while inspecting the overburden, you come across an isolated group of bare boulders piled up several feet away from a large mound of "classified" gravels, you are looking at the "coarse" and "fine" tailings piles of an earlier dredging operation. The "coarse" tailings are the piled-up boulders, which were too large to be sucked in by the intake of the previous dredger; the small boulders were moved away from the mining site by hand, while the larger boulders probably were winched from the hole with a "come-along" (more on that in Chapter Eleven). The mound of small, classified gravels will be the "fine" tailings from the operation; these were sucked into the vacuum system to eventually pour off the end of the sluice box, and thereby back into the river. Whenever you see "new" overburden, or tailings piles of the types just described, you can be pretty well assured that someone dredged this area a few years back. It may be wise to "write off" this location and look somewhere else.

The best way to determine the favorability of an area for dredging is to pry open and "snipe" some of the crevices you'll find in the bedrock. Crevices come in varying lengths and widths, and range from small "hairline" fissures to major cracks that extend from one river bank to the other. When present, pay careful attention to crevices that slant out into the middle of the stream to be covered by several feet of firmly packed overburden. If you recover substantial gold from the exposed portion of such a crevice near the bank, there may be a bonanza awaiting you if you bring in a dredge to remove the overburden from the deeply buried midstream section. (Figure 35)

Assuming now that you have located a promising crevice, you will need the next two pieces of gold-diving equipment, *rock hammer* and *pry bar*. These tools are necessary because any crevice that contains undisturbed gold will be filled with tightly impacted gravel that needs downright chiseling in order to get at the yellow stuff. Sometimes the rocks will be so tightly jammed in you'll think they were bonded together with epoxy glue!

The first step involved in cleaning a crevice is to remove any fine, light sands which often cover the upper portion. You can easily accomplish this by moving your hand rapidly back and forth over the crevice in a fanning motion. In the vernacular of gold-diving, this is known as "fanning the crack," and the turbulence so created will wash the lighter material out of the crevice, exposing any impacted material underneath. If there *is no* impacted gravel, the crevice probably has been cleaned by another sniper before you. It may be wise to pass up this spot and look for another.

When you encounter impacted gravel in a crevice, you will need to find a point where there is a slight break in the continuity of the "packing material." When you find such a spot, insert the point of your pry bar and use your rock hammer to drive it in. After you succeed in splitting off *one* of the rocks you will have a place to get some leverage with your pry bar. Drive the bar into the void created

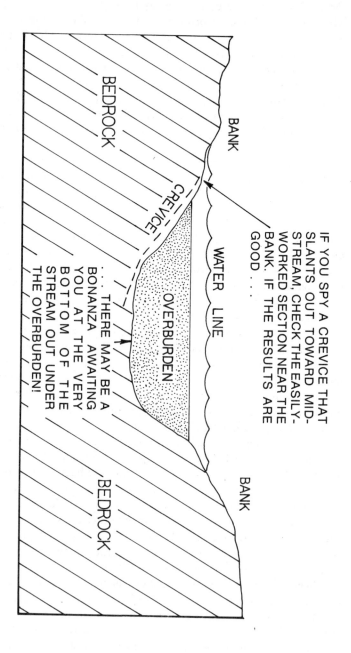

IF YOU SPY A CREVICE THAT SLANTS OUT TOWARD MID-STREAM, CHECK THE EASILY-WORKED SECTION NEAR THE BANK. IF THE RESULTS ARE GOOD . . . .

. . . THERE MAY BE A BONANZA AWAITING YOU AT THE VERY BOTTOM OF THE STREAM OUT UNDER THE OVERBURDEN!

Figure 35—Crevice slanting out toward mid-stream.

112

by the removal of the first rock, and then hammer sideways on the pry bar to loosen the adjacent rocks. Hammer in one direction, and then reverse the situation and hammer the other way. You will find that each time you remove any particular rock it will facilitate the removal of rocks along side of it. It will take time, but eventually you will get to the bottom of the crevice where it starts to narrow down. It is here where you will find the heavier materials that have been settling in the crevice over the years — black sands, old nails, bullets, buckshot, Chinese coins (no, I'm not kidding!), and last but certainly not least, GOLD. The gold will always be at the very bottom of the crevice, and now you will need your *long tweezers* to extract it. Believe me when I say you've never experienced a greater thrill in your life than that of picking nuggets out of a crevice and dropping them into your *sample bottle,* hearing that delightful PLUNK! every time a piece of gold hits the glass.

After the sizable gold has been removed from the crevice with tweezers, use your *crevicing tool* to loosen up any consolidated material remaining at the bottom. Next, stick the long nozzle of your *suction-gun* down to the bottom of the crevice and "suck up" the remaining heavy material; it may be necessary to do this several times. After you've accumulated a goodly amount of material, you can clean out the suction-gun and drop the contents into your *gold pan* for a speedy cleanup.

Let's take one final look at the crevice you've so painstakingly cleaned out. You think you've done a good job, eh? You say it's as empty as Mother Hubbard's cupboard? Well, think again — a crevice will never be completely cleaned until after you've taken your pry bar and split open the almost invisible hairline fissures that occasionally extend *beneath* the bottom of a crevice. It isn't easy cleaning a crevice down to absolute bottom, but the rewards will often make it worth your while. The hairline fissures of which I speak may widen out into a full-fledged pocket an inch or so below the floor of the normal crevice, and may yield excellent results. Many a beginning sniper has lost out on a beautiful nugget because he was unaware of this fact, and I'm passing this information along so that it won't happen to you.

If there's one thing the gold-diving world needs most, it's some sort of standard for determining the characteristics of a "rich assay" as far as a crevice is concerned. This will not be easy, because a crevice that's considered rich by one diver may well be "barren" by another man's standards. By *my* standards, if you recover anything over half an ounce of gold a day by sniping alone, you are on the right track. I'd advise you to spend more time and carefully snipe other crevices in the immediate area, and if all of them yield results similar to the first, it is time to consider bringing in your dredge. If you still question the richness of the area after sampling the crevices, try testing the overburden. If you're getting five or ten good-sized "colors" from *each pan* of general overburden (without being choosy about where you take the samples from), you have a "tiger by the tail." If for some reason you're *still* hesitant about bringing in your dredge at this point, just call me, and I'll come out and dredge the spot for you! (You can't blame a guy for *trying,* can you???)

So you've found yourself a genuine, honest-to-goodness hot spot! By this time you're probably ready to head back to civilization to settle your affairs, get your dredge out of mothballs, and bid a temporary farewell to a few old "flames." But wait just a minute. Have you remembered to take into consideration some of the cold, hard, logistics that are a part of every mining operation? Let's look at a few of them, and *then* make your final decision about working your "glory hole."

For the next couple of pages I'm mainly going to be talking to those individuals who are seriously interested in the recovery of paying quantities of gold. You recreation-minded gold-dredgers can follow along, too, in case you ever come down with a bad enough case of "the fever." If you make gold-dredging your hobby for a long enough period of time, sooner or later you're bound to try doing it for a living. Believe me, I know!

One very important factor to take into consideration is the *scope* of a potential dredging operation. It will be necessary for you to ask yourself the following questions, and be sure to give honest answers: "What am I getting myself into by taking on a project of the size I have in mind. Will I have enough *time* to see the project through to the end? Do I have the right *equipment* to get down to bedrock? Do I have enough *money in the bank* to see me through the 'poverty stage' while working my way down through the overburden?"

Those three italicized words — time, equipment, and money — are the three basic prerequisites for engaging in a mining venture. It doesn't matter if it is a dredging operation, a hardrock mine, or an oil well. If you can't meet all three prerequisites, you'd be better off devoting your energies elsewhere. But for now, let's get back to gold-dredging.

Accessibility has a great deal to do with any dredging venture. You may, indeed, have a dredging spot picked out that meets all the requirements of "El Dorado," but how difficult is it going to be to get equipment into the area? Are there any roads or trails nearby? If so, can a conventional vehicle get to the location without major difficulty?

Let's throw in a few other possibilities. Suppose your dredging spot is located a few miles up or downstream from the nearest road crossing. Are you prepared to float your equipment to the mining site on rafts as is so often necessary? What about rapids, narrows, and waterfalls that may block your way? To put it bluntly, can you transport your gear to your diggin's without killing yourself in the process?

Many times a dredging party (and it *takes* several people to conduct a sizable operation) will pick a mining spot so far out in the boondocks, its members will actually spend more time making supply runs than getting around to the business of gold-dredging. Thornton's Rule Number Four: "If it takes you *four* days of supply runs to carry in enough food and dredging gas to last for *three* days, you're in trouble from the very beginning." Of course, there's always the chance that you're working a real glory hole, but if that's the case, why not spend an ounce of gold a week and have your supplies airlifted in by helicopter? It's *the* thing, nowadays!

At this point I'm going to let everything "hit the fan," so to speak, by dropping one more bombshell. You may not like what I'm about to tell you, but it is important that you read it anyway and implant it in your mind.

Even if you discover an area which yields a considerable amount of gold from surface deposits, your discovery *still* may not be indicative of what lies at the bottom of the stream on bedrock. Never "count your chickens before they hatch" by spending your gold before you actually have it. True, bedrock may very well be fabulous, but then again. . . . This is where the element of plain, old-fashioned GOOD LUCK enters the picture, and don't let anyone tell you otherwise. If you're in the right place, at the right time, you're going to hit it. If the "fickle finger of fate" *isn't* on your side, you may as well go home and come back again tomorrow. It's as simple as that.

CHAPTER NINE
The Gold Pan
(and How to Use it)

Of all the dozens of pieces of mining equipment manufactured today, the one implement that still finds a prominent place in any type of gold prospecting is the common gold pan. Many people tend to associate the gold pan with grizzled old men who have long, bushy beards, floppy, tattered hats and an ever-faithful "Jenny mule" close at hand. Actually, the gold pan is used just as much by today's prospector as it was by the '49ers during the Gold Rush; it can safely be said that the improvements made on gold pans within the past few years have brought this "old standard" into the space age.

There are, perhaps, a few million people in this country who pan gold as a form of fun and recreation. After they've caught "the fever," they usually go in for bigger and more sophisticated equipment such as a gold dredge. From then on, their use of the gold pan will tend to be limited to use in sampling and cleanup procedures — that is, the final concentration of heavy materials that are caught in the riffles of a dredge's sluice box. Whatever *your* interest in the gold pan, it will be necessary for you to familiarize yourself with this unique instrument, together with the proper method of using it.

Gold pans come in varying sizes, styles, and also differ in the type of construction material used. Today you have a choice of either a steel pan, or one molded from high-impact plastic. As far as size goes, you can choose a small six-inch-wide pan, or one up to eighteen inches wide for panning large amounts of material; there are several intermediate sizes as well. The diameter of a gold pan may vary, but in operational theory they are all the same.

Perhaps the most common query to come from the lips of a beginning panner will be, "Which is better — a steel pan or a plastic pan?" I always give the same answer to this question: "It is really a matter of personal preference. If you learn to pan with a *steel* pan, that's what you'll stick with for the rest of your days. On the other hand, if you learned the basics of gold panning with a *plastic* pan, that's the one you'll swear by." Steel pans and plastic pans each have their own characteristics, and each is capable of performing tasks the other can't. For this reason, the professional prospector-sniper-dredger will have *both* types, and use the one that's most fitting for a given occasion.

The gold pan that has been around for the longest period of time is the basic steel pan. During the 1800's, these pans were forged one at a time by the local blacksmith, and were quite crude. Because the quality of the metal was so poor, the steel pans of olden days tended to wear out rather quickly; if you ever find one lying out in the backwoods, it will probably be filled with holes or worn spots. Today, steel gold pans are manufactured by a "spinning" process, and are made of a thicker metal than their early-day predecessors.

There are two principal styles of steel gold pans — those with a wide bottom and steep sides, and those with gently sloping sides leading down into a narrow, "drop-center." (Figure 36) Each style has its advantages. The drop-center pan has a prominent "ridge" where the sides drop down into the bottom, which acts as a gold trap. During the course of panning, any gold that is present will be forced against this ridge due to the swirling and sifting motions that are an integral part of the panning process. The small bottom diameter of the drop-center pan, however, does not allow you much room to swirl around the heavy materials that remain in your pan after the panning process is completed; the more you can spread this material out, the better you will be able to see any extremely small particles of gold. The steel pan that features steep sides with a wide bottom will solve this problem to a great extent, only this type of pan has no ridge to help catch the gold. A beginning panner is more apt to lose gold with this type of pan if he tilts it too steeply during the panning process.

All steel gold pans, when new, are coated with a film of oil to help prevent rust caused by moisture and condensation during transport. Before using a steel pan, it will be necessary to "burn off" this oil. If you use an oily pan in your prospecting efforts, many of

THIS IS THE
ORIGINAL GOLD PAN STYLE

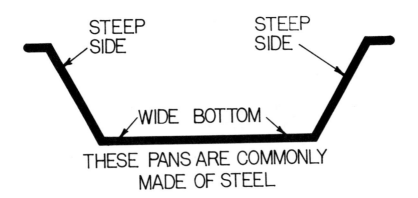

STEEP SIDE

STEEP SIDE

WIDE BOTTOM

THESE PANS ARE COMMONLY MADE OF STEEL

NEW-STYLE
"DROP CENTER" PAN

GENTLY SLOPING SIDES

RIDGE (GOLD TRAP)

DROP CENTER

DROP CENTER PANS ARE MADE IN BOTH STEEL AND PLASTIC VERSIONS

Figure 36—The two common styles of gold pans.

the smaller particles of gold will combine with the oil and wash right out of the pan with the waste material.

Burning off the oil (also known as "bluing" a pan) is most easily accomplished by placing the pan directly over an open fire. When the metal just starts to glow red, remove it from the fire and drop it into water. If the pan is a dark, steely-blue color, the oil has been completely burned and the pan can now be used. If there still are areas that haven't been completely blued, repeat the heating-dunking process until the bluing is uniform. (Incidentally, the resulting steely-blue coloration will also make your gold show up better!)

Steel gold pans have remained popular because they can be used for things other than gold panning. More than one dredger I know uses his steel pan as a shaving bowl, and some guys even go as far as using them as a frying pan to cook the mountain trout they occasionally catch. While I personally don't advocate this sort of thing, it can be done when you're in a pinch. These "side" applications are made possible because of the ease in re-gearing the steel pan for conventional mining applications — all you have to do is re-burn it. And while we're on the subject of re-burning, be sure to re-burn your pan at frequent intervals (during periods of heavy use, anyway) to drive off "body oils" which build up after continual contact with the hands.

The plastic gold pan made its first appearance in 1970, and has since become immensely popular. There are several reasons for this. First, being made of plastic, it is rust and corrosion-proof, meaning it does not have to be oiled; if it doesn't have to be oiled, it therefore doesn't have to be burned. Second, the surface of a plastic pan can be given a coarse "texturing" which will help gold stick to the bottom of the pan. The plastic pan also weighs much less than a steel pan, and it can be colored a permanent black so that even the tiniest particles of gold can easily be seen.

Since they are manufactured by an injection molding process, it is easy to form riffles in the sloping sides of a plastic pan. The riffles of a plastic pan help to prevent gold from washing out with the waste material, and can give even the beginning panner a certain degree of self-confidence. Old-timers often refer to these as "cheater riffles," because they allow the beginner to pan with nearly the same degree of efficiency it took them *years* to develop. Like their steel counterparts, plastic gold pans are offered in drop-center and wide-bottom configurations.

One of the great advantages plastic pans have over steel pans is that the plastic pan can be used for burning pieces of gold that are covered with mercury. Nitric acid has no effect whatsoever on a plastic pan, while steel is readily attacked. With plastic, it is also easy to employ a magnet for the purpose of removing black, magnetic sands that are found with placer gold. A powerful magnet of the type commonly used for this purpose would promptly "lock" onto a steel pan, making this task somewhat difficult.

A plastic gold pan will give you many years of carefree service if you take care of it. The type of plastic used for molding plastic pans is extremely resistant to shock and abrasion, but on occasion a prospector will experience — in the vernacular of nuclear power-plant technology — a "melt-down." Every so often, an unwary prospector will leave his plastic pan lying on the rear deck of his car on a bright sunny day, and as the light rays pass through the rear glass, extreme heat is created which causes the pan to melt down into an odd-shaped blob. As they say, to be forewarned is to be forearmed!

Plastic gold pans, like their steel bretherin, will eventually get contaminated with body oils, but it is obvious that you can't very well burn a plastic pan over a fire. Just what *do* you do? To start off, I'd advise you to get into the habit of carrying a small, unbreakable bottle of rubbing (isopropyl) alcohol on your trips, together with a box of cotton balls. When cleaning is necessary, simply moisten a cotton ball with rubbing alcohol and swab the inside of your pan. This process will effectively remove any oily contaminants which could lead to a partial loss of fine gold. (By the way — rubbing alcohol and cotton balls have another key application on prospecting trips, as you'll see in the next Chapter.)

In the following pages, I am going to teach you how to pan gold the way it *should* be panned. To be sure, you will run into gold panners out in the field who use methods totally unlike anything I'm going to present here, but this is understandable. Gold panning is an *art*, and as in any art form, no two people do it in exactly the same fashion.

Before you start to tackle the art of gold panning, select a location along the river bank where the water is at least six inches deep, with just enough of a current to wash away the lighter silts and gravels that will pour out of your pan as waste material. Another nice thing to have is a comfortable *rock* to sit on — it's no fun trying to pan gold while standing up!

Having selected the material you wish to process for gold, place it in your gold pan while taking care not to fill the pan too full. Three-quarters full is more than enough for a beginner. Place your pan under the surface of the water and vigorously shake it back and forth and side to side, but don't get *too* rambunctious, or you'll slosh material out of the pan.

After shaking the pan for ten seconds or so, start to move it in a gentle circular motion; this will cause the material in the pan to

move in a rotating motion which will break up much of the compacted material. After most of the compacted gravels have been
broken up, set the pan down under the surface of the stream and
physically work your fingers through the gravel; this action will
cause every bit of material in the pan to become exposed to the
water. As you work the material by hand, break up any remaining
lumps of compacted gravel and throw out all of the large rocks. If
there is clay adhering to any of the rocks, be sure to remove all of it
and dump it back into the pan; this is where much of your gold will
come from. If you are panning the roots of plants that grow at
water's edge, tear them completely apart down to the last minute
"thread."

The next step in the panning process is to work the smaller
rocks and pebbles up to the surface so that you can remove them
from the pan. Pick up your pan and once again shake it back and
forth under the stream. Dozens of small rocks will now be free to
work their way topside, and once they do you can stop and use the
side of your hand to "rake them off the top" and completely out of
the pan. Don't worry about raking out any gold; the same shaking
motion that causes the lighter rocks to surface also causes gold and
heavy materials to *sink* to the bottom of the pan. (Remember, gold
is eight times heavier than ordinary sand and gravel.) It may be
necessary to perform the "shake and rake" operation two or three
times to get all the small rocks out of your pan, but by doing so you
will make the next step of the panning process go all that much
easier.

It is now time to wash the remaining light, worthless material
out of your pan so that you can get down to the goodies underneath.
Hold your pan just barely under the surface of the stream, with the
side *furthest* from you about three inches lower than the nearer side;
next, start moving the pan in a circular motion combined with a
slight "thrust" each time the pan is moved to the outermost part of
its circle. If you do this right, each outward thrust will wash a small
amount of light material out of the lower side of the pan. (See Figure
37)

I realize how difficult it must be to visualize this action from the
simple illustration and text offered here, but rest assured it is not
that difficult. There is really only one critical point for you to
remember, and that's to be careful when tilting your pan. Not
enough tilt will make it difficult for you to wash out the unwanted
gravel, while *too much* tilt will let your gold slide right out of the
pan. Make sure that the lip of the pan on the down-tilted side is
always *higher* than the junction-point of the pan's bottom and
sidewall. (Figure 38)

After you have washed away the lighter gravel for approximate-

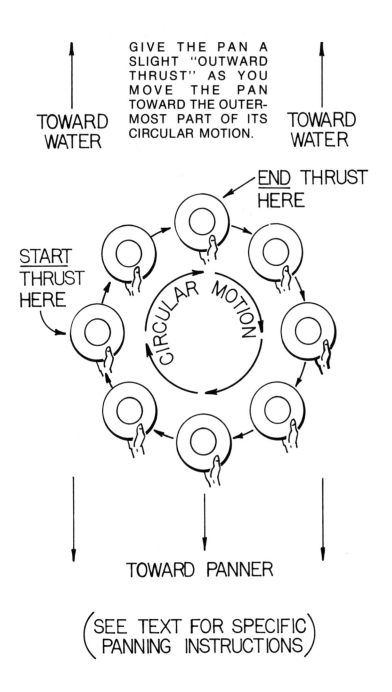

GIVE THE PAN A SLIGHT "OUTWARD THRUST" AS YOU MOVE THE PAN TOWARD THE OUTERMOST PART OF ITS CIRCULAR MOTION.

TOWARD WATER

TOWARD WATER

END THRUST HERE

START THRUST HERE

CIRCULAR MOTION

TOWARD PANNER

(SEE TEXT FOR SPECIFIC PANNING INSTRUCTIONS)

Figure 37—Diagram of the circular motion used in gold panning.

THIS PAN IS CORRECTLY TILTED; THE LIP OF
THE PAN IS HIGHER THAN THE "JUNCTION-
POINT" OF THE SIDEWALL AND BOTTOM.

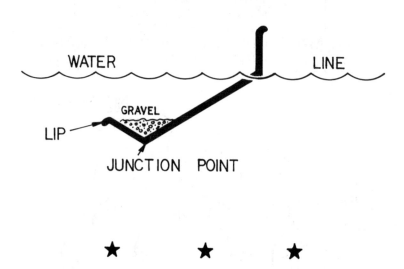

★　　　★　　　★

THIS PAN IS TILTED FAR TOO STEEPLY;
EVEN THE HEAVIEST OF GRAVEL
COMPONENTS (**INCLUDING** GOLD) WILL
SLIDE RIGHT OUT OVER THE SIDEWALL!

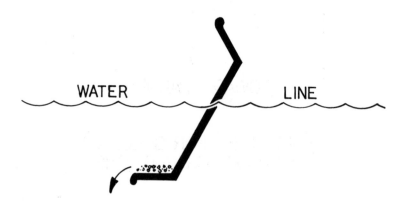

Figure 38—The correct (*and* incorrect) method of pan tilting.

ly ten seconds, stop to shake the pan back and forth for a brief moment; doing so will cause any "wandering" gold to settle back down onto the bottom of the pan where it belongs. Repeat the "circular thrust" motion to wash out more waste gravel, and again stop every so often to re-shake the pan. Keep up the washing process until you have worked your way down to the heavy, black sands which will be the last remaining substance in your pan after the panning process is completed. In addition to the goodly percentage of magnetic and non-magnetic iron ores, there will be traces of titanium, zircon, garnet, rutile, and monazite. All of these substances together are known as *concentrate*.

At this point you are ready to inspect your pan for traces of gold. Dip your pan into the river to pick up some water, and then swirl it around in the bottom of your pan to make the black sand spread out into a thin layer. If you spot any sizable flakes or small nuggets of gold, pick them out with a tweezers; your fingers will work if the pieces are large enough! After you've picked out the larger "chunkies," there will often be many tiny particles of gold that are too fine to be removed by tweezers. It is for this reason I suggest you learn and master the most difficult phase of the panning process, that of washing out all the black sand concentrate so that you have *pure gold* left as the end product.

Thoroughly shake the black sand down into the "corner" of your pan so that even the most minute particles of gold are on the very bottom. Next, tilt the furthermost edge of your pan and start dipping that side of the pan slowly back and forth in and out of the water. Each time the pan is pulled back from the water, a small amount of black sand will slide out over the lip of the pan; by using this method, the amount of material that slips out with each dip will be easily viewable. I say "viewable" because it is necessary to keep a very close eye on the concentrate as you do this. For some weird reason I can't explain, gold has a way of working its way toward the top of the concentrate during this process, and as soon as you see flakes of gold approaching the lip of the pan you should immediately stop to re-shake the gold back to the bottom. Repeat the dipping and shaking process until you have completely washed the black sands from your pan, or else 'til you've gotten it down to the point where there are only a couple of ounces of material left.

If you've panned off all your black sand and have pure gold left in the bottom of your pan, the easiest way to remove it is to use the "finger and bottle" method. Wet the tip of your index finger with saliva (plain water won't work, sorry) and touch it to the gold. The gold particles will adhere to the saliva, and you can then dip your finger into a sample bottle half filled with water. When the gold hits the surface of the water, it will drop off your finger, and you've now got your yellow stuff exactly where you want it.

For those of you who still have a bit of black sand mixed with your gold, you can use a magnet to remove the greater part of the unwanted substance. This is best accomplished with a plastic gold pan, but in case you don't own one . . . well, for this purpose, you *should*.

All of us have seen what happens when iron filings are poured onto a piece of stiff cardboard and a magnet run underneath. The filings move wherever the magnet is moved, and the same principle is used in separating magnetic black sands from gold. About the only prerequisite for performing this experiment is that the iron filings be dry, and the same is true in the case of black sand concentrates. To dry out your black sands, spread them out thinly in the bottom of a gold pan and set the pan in full sunlight; the heat of the sun will dry the sands in a couple of hours.

Once your black sands have dried completely, shake them down onto one side of your pan (a *plastic* one, remember) and keep the pan tilted. Touch a strong magnet to the underside of the pan right below the patch of concentrate; this will cause the black sand to immediately become attracted toward the magnet. Move the magnet in a circular motion under the concentrate to pick up all the magnetic material possible, and then pull the magnet — with the captured black sand — off to the high side of the pan. Any gold present will now be found lying on the low side of your pan in a virtually free state. You can then give it the "saliva treatment." If there is still residual black sand left after employing the magnet, it will be relatively light, non-magnetic hematite iron. It is a simple matter to pan off this material using the now-familiar dipping process; hematite iron is so light it usually will not require a force sufficient enough to wash gold out of your pan.

Today there tends to be a great deal of emphasis placed on "speed panning," which is not always a good thing. Many people can pan gold as fast as greased lightning, and there are even national and international "tournaments" to determine the "Gold Panning Champion of the World," etc. As far as this author is concerned, this sort of thing cannot be considered legitimate gold panning, because the contestants use plain, evenly sorted *light sand* salted with five or ten heavy nuggets which are impossible to lose. The average time it takes one of these so-called "experts" to pan down to the nuggets is twenty seconds, but if you were to hand them a pan filled with black sand, rocks, gobs of clay, roots, etc., I doubt if half of them could pan it down to the pure gold in twenty *minutes*! I'll get letters on *that* one.

If you are a newcomer to the fascinating world of gold panning, I strongly advise you to take it easy — for a while, at least — as far as speed is concerned; once you have acquired *skill* and *self-confidence,* you can start thinking about getting your name into the Guiness Book of World Records as "Gold Panner Extraordinaire!"

CHAPTER TEN
Diving Equipment (and Safety Habits) for the Underwater Prospector

Every underwater prospector I've had the pleasure of knowing derives countless hours of enjoyment from the use of his dredging equipment, be he professional, amateur, or in between. While many dredge operators partake in their hobby in shallow water areas by means of face mask and snorkel, the time will eventually come when *full-fledged* underwater mining activities take on special excitement (*and* challenge).

It is a common misconception that serious, underwater gold-dredging requires an extensive knowledge of diving techniques. Twenty-five years ago this was indeed true, as the only equipment available for underwater use then was the Self-Contained Underwater Breathing Apparatus (SCUBA). Even today, the proper use of SCUBA equipment (the system which requires the diver to wear metal, compressed air tanks on his back) is learned only after many hours of extensive, specialized instruction.

For the past ten or fifteen years, gold-dredging operations have employed what is known as the "Hookah dry-air system" of underwater diving. Hookah is ideally suited to underwater gold mining operations because an absolute minimum of equipment is required. The Hookah system consists of a small, lightweight air compressor that usually mounts right onto the same engine and pump assembly that powers your dredge. The output of the compressor goes through a short hose to a portable "receiver tank" which floats on the surface of the stream. The output of the receiver tank then goes through a long length of air hose to the diver underwater. The delivery end of the air hose is attached to a "check valve," which in turn is mounted onto a chest harness which the diver wears over his exposure suit. From the check valve, the air from the compressor is routed to the diver's "regulator," where the system terminates. (Figure 39)

Hookah is vastly superior to SCUBA for three principal reasons as far as gold-dredging is concerned. First, the diver does not need to wear large, bulky air tanks on his back; freed of this burden, the gold-dredger can maneuver himself into tight spots such as pockets between boulders, etc. With "backpack" tanks this

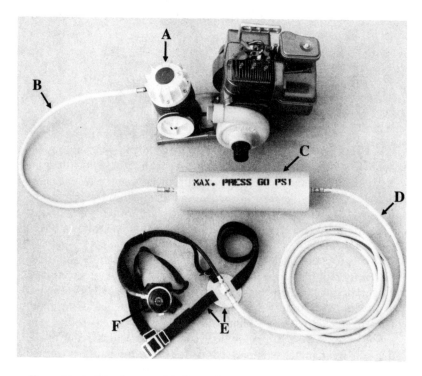

Figure 39—In this photographic "spread," you can see all the components of the Hookah dry-air system. The first component of the system is the compressor itself (A), a short length of connector hose (B), the reserve tank (C), a long length of air hose (D), the harness (E), and finally the regulator (F). Also required are two brass air fittings (hose to pipe) to adapt the connector hose (B) and the air hose (D) to their respective ends of the reserve tank.

would be impossible. Second, a diver using Hookah gear presents no resistance to the force of underwater currents which are often strong enough to rip SCUBA tanks right off a diver's back. (I definitely *do not* advocate diving in swift currents, but you can get caught by them *accidentally*.) And third, since the Hookah diver is connected to his compressor via a fixed length of air hose, he knows the exact extent of his maneuverability under the surface; a diver using SCUBA gear would be greatly tempted to wander off into areas where he might get caught by currents.

The Hookah dry-air system is also popular with gold-dredgers because they don't have to have air tanks refilled every hour or two, as is necessary with SCUBA. Since his air supply comes from a compressor mounted onto his dredge engine, a dredger can stay underwater and mine as long as his engine remains running; most gold-dredgers have a "buddy" diver working topside as a safety man to keep an eye on the compressor and to refill the gas tank as it gets low. (Use a funnel when refilling the gas tank on a running engine!)

Unlike SCUBA gear, Hookah equipment is relatively easy to use; a beginning gold-dredger can get the hang of Hookah diving in less than an hour. Very few gold-dredgers are "certified" divers, which is a necessity when using SCUBA gear. True, there are many basic safety precautions common to both SCUBA and Hookah, only in the case of Hookah the diver has much worry as far as *equipment* going bad on him.

Finally, Hookah equipment costs far less money than SCUBA gear. Not counting the air compressor (which usually is included in the dredge's purchase price), a diver can purchase a Hookah regulator, harness, air hose, and receiver tank for less than $125.

Now that we've discussed the advantages of the Hookah dry-air system, let's make a detailed examination of the actual equipment involved. Let's start out with the air compressor, and work our way down underwater to the regular.

Unlike large air compressors used to fill SCUBA tanks, the Hookah compressor is small, lightweight, and of simple design; it employs a flexible rubber diaphragm as the means of air displacement. As previously stated, Hookah compressors are usually mounted onto the dredge engine, and the power to drive the diaphragm comes from a V-belt and pulley that is mounted onto the engine's drive shaft in between the engine block and the back of the water pump.

The Hookah compressor is usually constructed of an aluminum alloy, making it resistant to the effects of the environment; one type of compressor commonly used on many gold dredges is shown in Figure 40. Weighing a mere thirteen pounds, the compressor pictured delivers two cubic feet of pure, clean air per

Figure 40—This is *one type* of diaphragm compressor commonly used in Hookah diving operations. Hookah compressors of the type shown here are simple, lightweight, and trouble free, needing virtually no maintenance whatsoever. While Hookah compressors all have the same basic features, physical appearance will differ from one manufacturer to another. (Photo courtesy of Keene Industries.)

minute; the air from a Hookah compressor needs no filtration before it goes underwater to the diver. A compressor of the type shown here uses no oil for lubrication, meaning there are no worries about breathing contaminated air. All parts in the Hookah compressor are prelubricated, and key components are treated with Teflon to insure a minimal amount of wear.

A portable Hookah compressor operates at fairly low pressures, the unit shown in Figure 40 delivering a maximum of 50 psi. Really, though, you don't *need* this much pressure, because a typical Hookah regulator (which you'll learn about shortly) delivers maximum displacement at pressures of approximately thirty psi. As long as you are dredging at depths of less than thirty-three feet, you should have to make no adjustments whatsoever to your air compressor. Even if you *did* have to go deeper than thirty-three feet, your regulator would only require another 14.7 psi to function properly, which amounts to one additional "atmosphere" of pressure. The compressor pictured here could "hack it," but certainly *no more* than this — at least not on a continuous basis.

The next key component in the Hookah dry-air system is the receiver tank, more commonly known as a "reserve tank." (Figure 41) The reserve tank resembles a miniature SCUBA tank, except it is much more compact. There are two small threaded holes in the reserve tank, one at each end. One is for air to enter as it comes from the output of the compressor via a short three or four-foot length of connector hose. The hole on the opposite end is the exit, and from here the air goes down underwater to the diver.

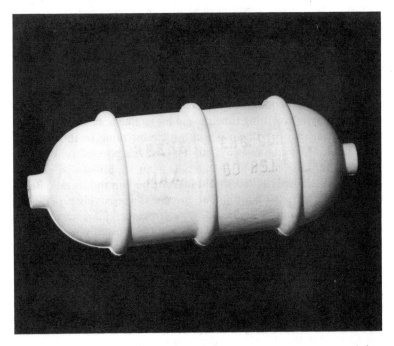

Figure 41—The reserve tank is an EXTREMELY important component of the Hookah dry-air system; it performs three critical functions, which are explained on page 134. The reserve tank shown here is of the type commonly used in recreational gold-diving operations. While all reserve tanks have the same basic functions, physical appearance will vary greatly from one manufacturer to another. (Photo courtesy of Keene Industries.)

The reserve tank performs three vital functions. First, it maintains a constant volume of air pressure by acting as a "reservoir" from which the diver draws his air. Every so often a portable gasoline engine — including those used on dredges — will run irregular, sometimes slowing down and speeding up for no apparent reason. (Well, there *are* reasons — sometimes a lousy batch of watered-down gasoline is to blame, other times the effects of heat, and occasionally "who knows what?") If your engine should start running slow, for example, your *compressor* is going to run slow, but by breathing out of a reserve tank instead of the actual output of the compressor you will always have that steady pressure which is required for comfortable breathing.

Not many dredgers realize it, but the air emerging from the output of their compressor often reaches a temperature of 140 degrees Fahrenheit! This is not sufficient to burn a man's flesh, but over an extended period of time it certainly doesn't benefit the insides of one's lungs. The reserve tank once again enters the picture, this time as a *cooling vessel* to reduce the temperature of the air before it goes to the diver. This is accomplished by merely allowing the reserve tank to float in the stream in which you are working; the cold water outside the tank will cool and condense the warm air inside. Don't worry about the reserve tank's "seaworthiness" — it is rugged enough to take it!

And finally, the most important function of all — the reserve tank will contain enough pressurized air to give the diver *forty-five* to *sixty seconds* breathing time should his engine or compressor ever fail. Equipment breakdown is not a pleasant thing to think about while blissfully dredging away, but it is always a possibility. Without a reserve tank to give him an emergency air supply, a diver whose power unit suddenly failed would literally be "up the creek." Being caught underwater with nothing to breathe is a terrifying experience, even when working in shallow depths. However, if a reserve tank is used, a diver can make it back to the surface usually with air left over.

Once the air supply leaves the output of the reserve tank, it travels down underwater to the diver via a special, non-kink, non-collapsible, floating air hose. Hookah hose usually is constructed of vinyl plastic, and is immune to the effects of cold water, hot sun, oil, gasoline, and just about anything that man or nature can dish out. It *has* to be, for the diver's life depends on it.

Most air hose used for Hookah diving has an inside diameter of ⅜ inches, and the walls are reinforced with nylon to make the hose super-durable. The wall will be quite tough, yet flexible at the same time. One would assume that the flexibility of Hookah air hose would let it kink and possibly shut off the diver's air flow, but this is not the case — I've never yet seen a good quality Hookah hose kink-up, *or* collapse.

Hookah air hose also floats, eliminating the possibility of a diver getting entangled in his own air line while working on the bottom. For example, if a dredger is working in *ten* feet of water but is using a *thirty*-foot length of hose, the excess twenty feet of air hose will float on the surface completely out of his way.

The delivery end of the air hose terminates at the diver's "harness." The harness serves two principal functions. First, it keeps the diver's air hose from interfering with him when he is working underwater. The harness has a "backplate" which is automatically positioned over the center of the diver's back when the harness is donned. The "check valve" that was mentioned earlier acts as a junction point for the air hose terminus and the hose that goes on to the regular, and is mounted onto the backplate. (Figure 42)

Since the input hose that leads to the diver's regulator is attached to the air hose *indirectly* by means of the check valve, the harness is able to perform its second function — this is to prevent pull on the regulator. If the air hose coming from the surface should, for example, accidentally get wrapped around a boulder, the harness would absorb the shock and the regulator would not be ripped from the diver's mouth as would be the case if the harness were *not* employed.

The check valve itself also performs a function, and an extremely vital one at that. It acts as a "safety gate" to shut down the air system should a break ever occur in the air line somewhere between the output of the compressor and the input of the check valve. Let's refer to Figure 43 for the details.

The interior of a check valve consists, essentially, of a spring-loaded ball which ordinarily fits tight against a "seat" on the inside of the valve housing. When air under pressure is introduced into the input of the valve, the ball is forced open and air is allowed to pass through the valve and out into the regulator hose connected to the output end. So long as a steady flow of pressurized air is passing through the valve, the ball will remain open. However, if by some one-in-a-million chance the diver's air hose were to break, air will cease to flow into the valve and the spring-loaded ball will be forced back against the seat, preventing the diver from breathing in a large amount of water which would otherwise be sucked into the regulator hose. If such a thing ever happened *without* a check valve in place in the air line, the diver would very likely panic and wind up in a desperate situation; as any experienced diver will tell you, panic is one of the leading causes of underwater death. You can therefore see why I give the following advice: NEVER, EVER, dive without a harness and check valve!

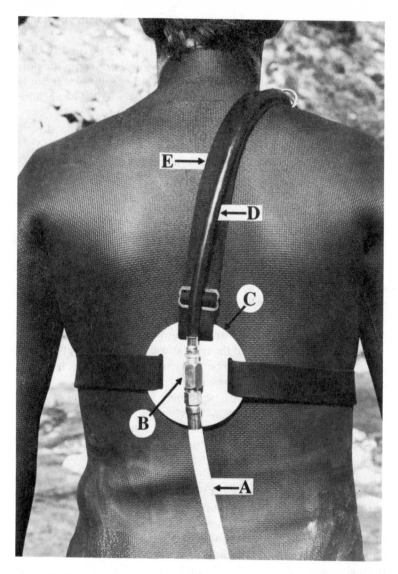

Figure 42—Even though this photograph of a diver's back may not appear to be overly interesting, it *does* show a number of important components that are part of the Hookah dry-air system; of primary importance is the air hose terminus on the harness backplate. To start off, air from the reserve tank enters the picture at the bottom, via the *air hose* (A); it then goes into the input end of the *check valve* (B), which is permanently mounted onto the harness *backplate* (C). From the check valve, the air goes into the *regulator hose* (D), up along the shoulder section of the *harness webbing* (E), and finally terminating at the diver's regulator (not shown in picture). The entire harness and check valve assembly has one principal function: IT'S FOR SAFETY, and the diver who ventures beneath the waters of a mountain stream *without* this apparatus is really asking for trouble!

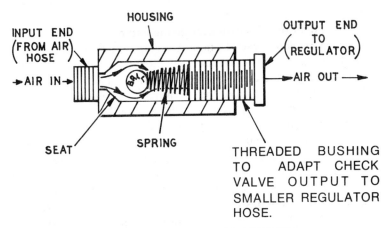

INPUT END
(FROM AIR HOSE)

→ AIR IN →

HOUSING

OUTPUT END
TO
(REGULATOR)

→ AIR OUT →

SEAT

SPRING

THREADED BUSHING
TO ADAPT CHECK
VALVE OUTPUT TO
SMALLER REGULATOR
HOSE.

THIS CHECK VALVE IS "OPEN";
AIR IS ENTERING AT THE INPUT
END, FORCING THE SPRING-
LOADED BALL AWAY FROM THE
SEAT, AND PASSING ON
THROUGH TO EMERGE AT THE
OUTPUT END.

★   ★   ★

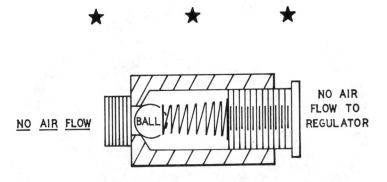

NO AIR FLOW

NO AIR
FLOW TO
REGULATOR

THIS CHECK VALVE IS **CLOSED;**
THERE IS NO AIR ENTERING THE
INPUT END, ALLOWING THE
SPRING TO FORCE THE BALL
TIGHT AGAINST THE SEAT. THIS
ACTS AS A "SAFETY GATE" BY
PREVENTING THE DIVER FROM
BREATHING IN WATER, SHOULD
HIS AIR HOSE BREAK.

Figure 43—Diagram of the insides of a check valve.

So far in our discussion of diving equipment I've brought up the word *regulator* several times. A regulator is a respiration device which, for lack of better terminology, "regulates" the amount of air that is taken in by a diver each time he inhales. The word "inhale" is used merely to present the theory; in reality, a regulator is an *oral* breathing device which is worn in the mouth. This is necessary because the diver's nose is covered by his face mask.

The regulator that is used in Hookah diving is a "second stage" regulator consisting of the actual oral breathing apparatus itself; there are no complicated valve assemblies of the type that mount onto the tops of SCUBA tanks. (Figure 44) The sheer simplicity of the Hookah regulator can be appreciated all that much more when I tell you that it contains only *six* principal parts — the pin valve, housing, diaphragm, mouthpiece, exhaust port, and clearing button.

As pressurized air emerges from the output of the check valve, it travels through a short length of hose which terminates at the *pin valve*; this assembly is mounted onto the side of the regulator *housing*. A long steel "pin" protrudes from a small circular opening in the valve assembly and sticks out into the center of the housing.

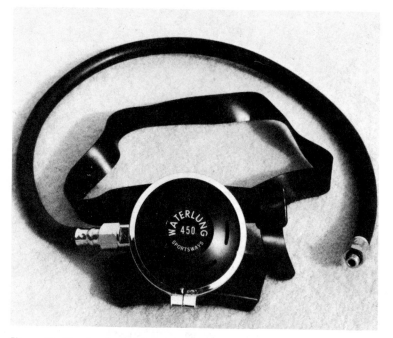

Figure 44—The Sportsways "Waterlung 450" is a good example of a second-stage regulator used in Hookah diving operations. A regulator of this type requires no complicated valve assemblies of the type found on SCUBA tanks; rather, it screws directly into the output end of the check valve.

Just inside the "face" of the regulator is a thin rubber *diaphragm* with a rigid metal centerplate; the diaphragm is in exact opposition to the *mouthpiece* from which the diver breathes. When the diver wishes to take in air, he sucks into the mouthpiece; this draws the diaphragm toward the mouthpiece, and as the diaphragm is pulled back, the metal centerplate contacts the valve pin and deflects it inward against its circular opening. When the valve pin is deflected, the valve is opened and air enters the housing and goes out through the mouthpiece to the diver. Each time the diver exhales, the diaphragm is pushed back toward the front of the regulator housing and the pin valve closes. The spent air will then force open a rubber gasket that seals the *exhaust port* and exit the housing through that opening. (See Figure 45)

Quite frequently, a small amount of water will get inside the air hose and reserve tank during the hooking-up process, and it is the function of the regulator's *clearing button* to remove this moisture before you actually place the regulator in your mouth and dive. The clearing button is located on the face of the regulator housing, and when depressed, it causes the diaphragm centerplate to push against the valve pin and send a surge of air through the housing and out of the mouthpiece. By pushing the clearing button and holding it for a few seconds, any water inside the air hose, reserve tank, or regulator will quickly be blown out.

Now that you understand the Hookah dry-air system, let's take a look at some other pieces of diving equipment that are commonly employed in gold-dredging operations. I've already discussed the principles of the underwater diving suit, face mask and snorkel, etc., in a previous Chapter, but as far as actually *purchasing* these pieces of equipment goes, there are a few additional things you'll need to know.

I strongly advise you to be wary of the "cheapie" diving suit — that's the one you'll see advertised for fifty dollars, perhaps. As far as protecting you from cold water it does its job well, but the "cheapie" suit will quickly wear out and come apart at the seams. Insist on a suit made of high-quality neoprene rubber; if you purchase a suit manufactured by one of the major diving equipment companies, you can be pretty well assured of getting good material. Also, make sure that every seam in your suit is *lock-stitched*; a seam sewn in this manner will not come apart after a few weeks of use. And last but not least, try to purchase a suit that is completely *lined* on the interior with nylon or other related material. A suit which has bare neoprene exposed on the insides is incredibly difficult to get in and out of, and it will often be necessary to sprinkle talcum powder on your body to "lubricate" yourself before donning the suit. All the features mentioned here also apply to neoprene gloves, hood, and

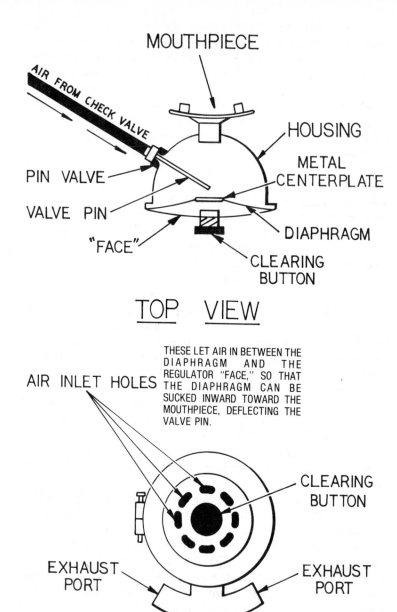

MOUTHPIECE

AIR FROM CHECK VALVE

HOUSING

METAL CENTERPLATE

PIN VALVE

VALVE PIN

"FACE"

DIAPHRAGM

CLEARING BUTTON

TOP VIEW

AIR INLET HOLES — THESE LET AIR IN BETWEEN THE DIAPHRAGM AND THE REGULATOR "FACE," SO THAT THE DIAPHRAGM CAN BE SUCKED INWARD TOWARD THE MOUTHPIECE, DEFLECTING THE VALVE PIN.

CLEARING BUTTON

EXHAUST PORT

EXHAUST PORT

EXHAUST SYSTEM

FRONT VIEW

Figure 45—The insides of a "second stage" Hookah regulator.

booties that are accessory items to the suit.

A good face mask is like a pair of eye glasses — it must be correct for the individual who will be wearing it or else the entire principle is defeated. I'm not implying that it's necessary to have your face measured for a diving mask, but it *will* be necessary for you to try several different styles and shapes of masks before you purchase one. A diving mask must fit snugly (yet comfortably) around the contours of your face, while allowing a wide field of vision.

The first thing to look for in a face mask is a *tempered faceplate.* NEVER buy a mask which has a plain glass faceplate — if the glass should break as the result of an underwater accident, there is a good chance of getting some of it in your eyes. A tempered faceplate will not break, but will "fracture" across the face of the mask just like the safety glass used in the windshields of automobiles.

After you've located the face masks with tempered faceplates, try on the various models until you find one that features wide vision *and* a comfortable fit around the edges. Try to avoid a mask with sealing edges made of stiff rubber — after a short time they will literally "dig" into your face, and that *hurts!* A good way to find the right mask is to place the mask against your face, breathe in deeply through your nose and remove your hands — if the mask "molds" itself to your face without letting any air in around the edges, you've found what you're looking for.

When you are "sniping" in an area looking for likely crevices, you will get much use from your snorkel. The snorkel is a relatively inexpensive piece of diving gear, and a good one can be purchased for less than five dollars. But once again, there are things to watch out for. Perhaps the most important piece of advice I can pass along about the snorkel is to NEVER purchase one that has a "ball and socket" valve at the end that sticks up out of the water. The ball and socket snorkel was originally designed to prevent water from entering the snorkel tube when the diver was entirely below the surface; when submerged, the ball will float upward trying to get to the surface but will be stopped by the socket, thus forming a seal. Now this may sound fine and dandy, but it's *not* — the ball has a tendency to float upward against the socket at inopportune moments, and if a seal is formed when a diver is taking in air and getting ready to submerge, he may be on his way to the bottom with far less air in his lungs than he originally anticipated. When the diver finally realizes this, he is well under the surface of the water and may conceivably panic.

Contrary to popular belief, rubber swim fins are rarely employed in gold-dredging operations. The purpose of the fin is to help a diver move rapidly under the surface, but in a dredging operation the diver is working in one fixed location for hours on end. The only time swim fins are used is while traveling back and forth from crevice to crevice, such as during sniping operations.

Once a sniper has located a good gold area and starts dredging, he will definitely need *some* type of footwear; quite frequently he will choose a pair of rugged, U.S. Army surplus "combat boots." Combat boots stand up well against the effects of water, but more important, they protect the diver's feet from the bumps and knocks that are a part of every dredging operation. If you can't find a pair of combat boots, buy a pair of oversized "highwall" tennis shoes and wear them over your neoprene booties — they don't give much protection against knocks, but they're better than nothing.

As much as I hate doing it, I must introduce you to the subject of *diving weights.* It is a sad fact, indeed, that a diver wearing a full exposure suit will literally float like a cork, and some type of weight is necessary to keep him on the bottom so that he can maneuver the intake of his dredge. The most popular (???) diving weight is made of plain, unglamorous *lead*, and believe me when I say it's no fun hassling with them.

Lead weights are cast in varying sizes, and usually weigh from five to fifteen pounds. They have two slits in them so that a rugged, nylon "weight belt" can be threaded through. The weight belt is worn around the diver's mid-section and not necessarily over the exact waistline. All weight belts have a quick-release buckle so that the belt can be jettisoned in case of emergency.

Lead weights can be purchased ready-cast, or else you can purchase a weight mold and cast them yourself. The latter method may sound like a lot of trouble, but once you've gone into a dive shop and checked the prices of ready-made weights you'll have second thoughts. You can purchase scrap lead at a local junk yard, and after taking into account the cost of the raw lead *and* the mold you'll *still* save money by casting them yourself!

The amount of lead a diver needs around his waist to keep him submerged depends upon his body weight, and of course, whether or not he is wearing an exposure suit. As strange as it may seem, a heavy person with a husky, muscular build will be extremely buoyant and actually require *more* weights than a skinny person. Normally you'd expect a heavy person to sink and a thin person to float, but it works the exact opposite. It is not uncommon for a husky diver to need upwards of seventy-five pounds of lead, and a *really* heavily built guy will need a hundred pounds together with a second weight belt on which to place all that lead! Determining the amount of weight that is necessary for you personally can only be accomplished by the trial-and-error process; after several experimental dives, you'll have a good idea as to the exact amount of weight necessary to keep you under. As a general starting figure, I'd take along fifty pounds of lead and work your way up from there.

As in any underwater diving situation, a prospector who ventures beneath the waters of a mountain stream in search of gold will need to be aware of the "hazards of the deep." There are many laws, clearly interpreted and universally recognized, that are the same whether you're diving in the ocean, a lake, a swimming pool, or a gold-bearing river.

The major diving hazard that is likely to confront the gold-dredger is *air embolism*. This extremely dangerous condition is caused when a diver holds his breath while coming back up to the surface. NEVER hold your breath while surfacing, even if you're only coming up from shallow depths!!! Memorize the following facts, and *think* about them each time you dive. . . .

When a diver is submerged, the air in his lungs is under pressure. Everything is fine so long as he is underwater where the pressure is high, but if a diver surfaces and *holds* his breath, the lesser pressures encountered on the way up will create an imbalance in his lungs. The air in the diver's lungs will now be of greater pressure than that of the water outside, and air will force its way into the aevoli. (Aevoli is the physiological term for the lungs' tiny air sacs where venous blood sheds waste carbon dioxide and picks up fresh oxygen.) Once in the aevoli, the air has officially entered the circulatory system and will be carried to the heart; from here the air will be pumped to all parts of the diver's body, and once it reaches the brain it can cause unconsciousness or even *death*.

It is very easy to avoid air embolism simply by remembering these three basic rules: (1) Never ascend faster than the exhaust bubbles from your regulator; (2) do not ascend faster than twenty-five feet per minute, and (3) remember to breathe in and out *normally* on the way up!

One of the most dreaded hazards related to diving is *nitrogen narcosis*, commonly referred to as "Rapture of the Deep." In reality, the average gold-diver needn't worry about getting a case of nitrogen narcosis, as this condition is encountered at depths of one hundred feet or more. (Very few of you will ever be going *that* deep, believe me!) At such great depths a diver *will* (not maybe) act like he is intoxicated, and will be utterly wreckless and unable to look after himself. Only a very skilled diver should attempt to go this deep.

A condition more likely to be encountered by the gold-dredger is *decompression sickness*, more commonly known as "the bends." This condition is brought on when a diver has been below depths of thirty-three feet without "decompressing" on the way up.

The bends is caused by the accumulation of nitrogen bubbles in the diver's bloodstream. At depths of less than thirty-three feet, the nitrogen bubbles are very tiny and are carried away by the circulatory system to eventually dissipate. However, at depths *greater* than thirty-three feet the body is subjected to one additional "atmosphere" of pressure, and the bubbles become large enough to press on nerve endings or else interfere with circulation. In extreme cases, the bubbles can completely block the blood vessels or else replace the blood entirely, causing death.

If it is ever necessary for you to dive at depths greater than thirty-three feet, standard U.S. Navy Decompression Tables MUST be strictly adhered to. To "decompress" means to pause and rest at certain depth intervals when making an ascent, to allow your body to re-adjust to the lesser pressures the human mechanism is normally accustomed to. The duration of each rest stop has been exactly calculated in the Decompression Tables, and it will be necessary for you to use a depth gauge and underwater watch when diving in waters deep enough to warrant decompression.

It is extremely important that a diver *never* wear earplugs when venturing beneath the surface; earplugs will prevent the equalization of pressure between the middle ear and the world outside. A diver who wears earplugs is inviting serious trouble in the form of pain, bleeding, and the possible rupture of his eardrums. Leave your earplugs at home!

If you are going to be gold-dredging for extended periods of time — particularly during midsummer when the rivers warm up a bit — make every effort to protect yourself from the unpleasant condition known as "divers' ear." Divers' ear is caused by the growth of a warm-water fungus inside the ear, and can be excruciatingly painful. This condition is commonly prevalent among the more professional gold-dredgers who are in the water for eight to ten hours a day straight, but it can be picked up by the hobbyist as well.

Believe it or not, divers' ear can effectively be prevented by the use of the same commodities that remove body oils from a plastic gold pan — I speak of *rubbing alcohol* and *cotton balls.* At the end of every dredging day — *without fail* — lightly moisten a cotton ball with rubbing alcohol and use it to swab out the accessible portions of your ears. This will kill any waterborne fungus before it gets the chance to work its way further into your ears and multiply. It takes only a couple of minutes to do this simple, "preventative maintenance," yet it can save you days or even weeks of pain that is associated with divers' ear.

Any underwater diving activity (and particularly gold-dredging) drains a substantial amount of energy from the human body, and it is important for the diver to be in good physical condition. Persons who have heart trouble, emphysema, chronic bronchitis or other lung diseases, asthma and other sinus conditions, perforated eardrum, non-correctible vision, intestinal trouble, hemorrhoids, etc., should consult their physician before undertaking any dredging operations; excessively overweight persons should also follow their doctor's advice. There are many thousands of individuals with one (or more) of the aforementioned conditions who partake in the sport of diving with no ill effects, but they are pushing their luck. A physical examination is far cheaper than spending weeks in a hospital recovering from a diving-related accident.

Even if you are in good physical condition, make every effort to treat your body well when out on a dredging expedition. Always get a good night's sleep, preferably in a nice, warm sleeping bag; after maneuvering the intake of a dredge all day — plus getting rid of unwanted boulders — your body needs several hours to recuperate. If you should pick up some sort of "creeping crud" in the form of cold or flu, stay out of the water until you have fully recovered. It is advised that you stay away from heavy, gas-forming foods and stick to high-protein provisions. If it is ever necessary for you to take some type of medication, don't dive until it has worn off. Be sure to treat any cuts, scratches, or bruises as soon as possible.

Gold-dredging, as stated a bit earlier, is a physically demanding activity that puts the body through its paces; it is therefore important that you avoid "overdoing it." Do not attempt to dredge for extremely lengthy periods, but rather, stay underwater for *two hours* at a time and then let your "safety man" go down for two hours. By setting up a "two hours on, two hours off" routine, your body will get a chance to replenish its energy by the time it's your turn to go back down again. As a result, you won't feel like a "walking zombie" at the end of each dredging day.

The last of my safety recommendations relate to the actual river environment itself. Mountain streams, depending upon the time of year, can be swift, savage, and deadly. Always treat a river with *respect*, and don't attempt to cheat on Nature's rules.

A river is full of hazards that the gold-dredger must learn to avoid. Among the more dangerous are swift currents, cold water temperatures, deep holes, caving banks, and particularly shifting boulders. Because of the potential dangers, it is important for your topside safety man to *own his own regulator and diving gear* and have it hooked up to the air system at all times; if you were to ever get into trouble while working underwater, your buddy could dive in and come to your aid. As an example, a great many gold-dredgers will undermine a large boulder in hopes of recovering gold from its base. Sometimes a diver will dredge too much gravel from around a boulder, causing it to cave in on him. If this ever happened while diving *without* a safety man, a diver would be in a very grave situation. If he couldn't free himself by the time his gas tank ran dry . . . well, that's not a pleasant subject to write about.

Never attempt to dredge in a river when it is flowing murky, such as after a period of heavy rainfall. Not only will the currents be fast and dangerous, you'll also be lucky if you can see your hand in front of your face! Good visibility is a MUST while gold-dredging — in addition to being able to see *what it is* you're dredging, you'll also spot any potential hazards and steer clear of them. Take special note of these safety precautions when dredging in isolated areas — emergency help may often be hours away, and by the time it arrives it may be too late. When diving safety is concerned, there is no such thing as being "too safe!"

If I've managed to frighten you with some of the information presented in this Chapter, rest assured that it wasn't my intention. I should point out that if you learn how to correctly use your diving equipment, if you avoid the common hazards of the deep, if you take proper care of your body and use plain, common sense when working in any river environment, you'll have no trouble whatsoever when pursuing what I consider to be the world's *number one* hobby activity — that's gold-dredging!

CHAPTER ELEVEN
How to Successfully Conduct a Dredging Operation

At this late point in time I am going to make a number of assumptions. First, I'm going to assume that you've bought a gold dredge. Second, I'll take it for granted you've purchased Hookah diving gear. And finally, I have every reason to believe you've located an underwater deposit of gold-bearing material and that you're "champing at the bit" in anticipation of getting started.

As your eyes scan over the location you've selected for dredging, a number of questions will come to mind. Among the more common will be, "Where exactly do I start dredging? Where should I position my dredge in the river? How do I get rid of all the large boulders I'll encounter on my way down to bedrock?" The answers to these questions — and many others — will be found in the following pages.

Contrary to popular opinion, deep water is *not* a prerequisite for dredging operations. Any stream area that is deep enough to fully submerge the foot valve so that it doesn't draw air from the surface is deep enough to run a dredge. I do admit that when using certain types of dredges (below-water power-jet rigs, for example) it *is* desirable to work in water at least two feet deep so that the jet-tube won't scrape on the bottom of the stream. In contrast, a suction nozzle dredge can be set up any place where the water is deep enough to clear the bottom of the flotation rigging. This author, on more than one occasion, has operated a four-inch surface dredge — the suction nozzle type — in small creeks with only *six inches* of clearance between my inner tube flotation rigging and the bottom of the stream!

About the only major thing to watch for when operating a dredge in shallow water is the screened intake of your foot valve. Many times, the valve will rest directly on the bottom of the stream, and is subject to attack by two stubborn adversaries. The first is "flow sand," which moves along the bottom of a stream with the current. The second is vegetable matter, which travels virtually in the same manner.

Flow sand can either be a minor nuisance or a major headache, depending upon how long it takes the sand to bury your foot valve. Some streams have so much flow sand you'll have to "excavate" your foot valve every ten minutes, while in others you can dredge for hours before the valve is buried. In either case, the final results are the same — reduced water intake into the pump, less gallonage going into the eduction device, and therefore reduced suction. Also, the abrasive effects of sand aren't very beneficial to the interior of your water pump. While a centrifugal pump will pass a small amount of sand without being harmed, too much sand can cause extensive damage. As an example, I once saw a pump housing that was scoured *paper thin* because the dredger who owned it allowed his foot valve to rest in a position where it pulled in more sand than water. This happened after only four or five hours of use!

Vegetable matter — principally in the form of roots, leaves, and algae — also travels along the bottoms of streams, and can be more pesky than flow sand. The suction that's created by a dredge's pump intake seems to "draw" vegetable matter toward the foot valve screen like a magnet. Unlike flow sand which merely buries the foot valve, vegetable matter can clog the holes of the intake screen to such an extent that water intake is cut practically to zero. When this happens, it is advisable to shut down the engine so that the pump doesn't run partially dry. You can then take your time and do a thorough job of picking out the "impacted" material.

You can prevent flow sand and vegetable matter from plaguing your pump intake by constructing a small "diversion dam" just upstream from the foot valve. Use any rocks or small boulders which are handy and pile them up to form a wall which slants downstream and off to one side of the foot valve. The current will cause flow sand, vegetable matter and any other unwanted substance to be deflected off to the sidelines where they won't affect your operations. (Figure 46)

You can also use a plain, old-fashioned bucket to protect your

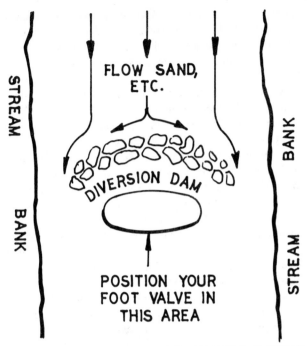

STREAM BANK

STREAM BANK

FLOW SAND, ETC.

DIVERSION DAM

POSITION YOUR FOOT VALVE IN THIS AREA

WHEN FLOW SAND OR WATER-BORNE VEGETABLE MATTER IS A PROBLEM, CONSTRUCT A "DIVERSION DAM" TO DEFLECT THESE UNDESIRABLES OFF TO THE SIDELINES. USE ANY ROCKS OR SMALL BOULDERS WHICH ARE HANDY.

Figure 46—Diagram of flow sand "diversion dam."

foot valve. Dig a small hole into the bottom of the stream and insert the bucket so that half of it is buried and half of it protruding. Now place your foot valve into the bucket. (Figure 47) Flow sand, etc., will travel *around* the bucket while the foot valve inside pulls in only clean, clear water. Eventually, sand may build up on the lee side of the bucket, not unlike gravels on the downstream side of a large boulder; you'll still get in quite a bit of dredging time before having to stop and move it away.

There is a right way (*and* a wrong way) of going about any task imaginable; the same applies to a gold-dredging operation. For example, far too many gold-divers will plop their dredge anywhere in the midst of a gold-bearing deposit and start moving gravel in a random fashion. An operation such as this is doomed to failure from the beginning.

A gold-dredger should always start his mining operation on the *downstream* end of a deposit and work his way upstream. By operating in this fashion, the gravel and overburden you move as you work your way upstream will thereby fill in holes you've already cleaned out. Many beginning dredgers are not aware of this, and will start their operation by moving gravel at the upper end of the deposit. As they move further downstream, they suddenly realize they will have to dredge *their own tailings* out of the way before they can even start in on the regular gravel. Save yourself a lot of hassle by doing it the *right* way, the *first* time!

The positioning of a dredge in a stream is extremely important, but unfortunately, not always an easy task. Most gold dredges come with ten to fifteen feet of suction hose, which means you have only this much leeway (unless your engine and pump is powerful enough to allow the addition of extra hose) to find a suitable spot for the dredge where the current will carry away the tailings. Very often, the most desirable location for the dredge will be just beyond the limit of your suction hose, or else will leave you only a couple of feet of hose with which to work. If you move the dredge in closer to your mining spot, you may find that the tailings will pour off the end of the sluice box and right back into your hole! You frequently will have to compromise by selecting a location where the current will

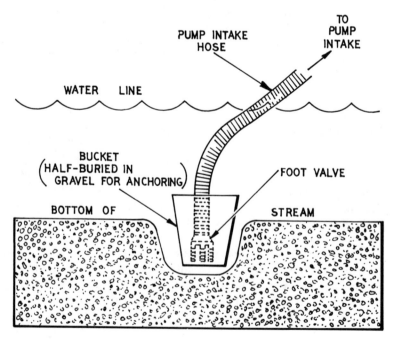

Figure 47—Diagram of "bucket-type" foot valve protector.

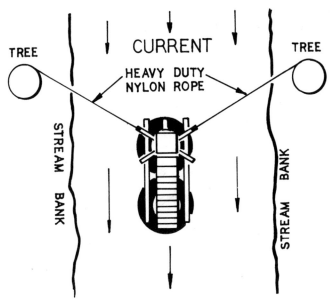

IF YOU FIND IT NECESSARY TO POSITION YOUR
DREDGE IN A FAST-WATER AREA, USE A PAIR OF
WATERPROOF, HEAVY-DUTY NYLON ROPES TO
SECURE THE RIG SO THAT YOU WON'T LOSE IT!
TIE THE UPSTREAM END OF YOUR DREDGE TO A
STURDY TREE TRUNK ON EACH BANK.

Figure 48—Securing a dredge in a fast-water area.

carry away *most* of the tailings while allowing you just enough slack
in the suction hose to easily maneuver the intake. If your engine and
pump is capable of "hacking it," by all means purchase an extra ten
or fifteen feet of suction hose so that you'll have enough for any
situation you may run into.

If it is necessary for you to position your dredge in the midst of
a fairly swift current, I'd advise you to securely tie the dredge to permanently fixed objects on each stream bank. A set of sturdy tree
trunks will do nicely, coupled with two fifty-foot lengths of high-
quality, waterproof nylon rope. Tie one end of the ropes onto the
upstream end of the dredge (as shown in Figure 48) and run the opposite ends to the anchor points up on the banks. It should be noted
that this method of dredge tying won't work in all situations.
Sometimes it will be necessary for you to slant the dredge in a particular direction so as to allow you maximum maneuverability of
your intake, and it is *not* uncommon for a dredger to position his rig
on an angle somewhat *diagonal* to the flow of the current in order to
get the most from his suction hose. If this becomes a necessity,
fasten one tie rope to the upstream end of the dredge, and the second

151

rope on the downstream, discharge end. (Figure 49) Now all you do is tie the ropes to fixed objects on the shore as usual.

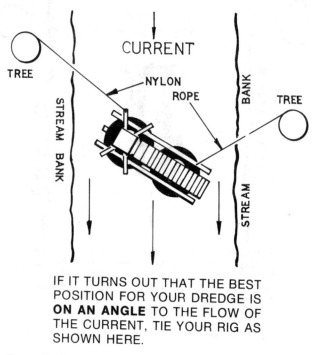

IF IT TURNS OUT THAT THE BEST POSITION FOR YOUR DREDGE IS **ON AN ANGLE** TO THE FLOW OF THE CURRENT, TIE YOUR RIG AS SHOWN HERE.

Figure 49—Securing a dredge on an angle to the current flow.

A modern gold dredge can truly be called a "dream machine," but when it comes right down to it, a gold dredge is basically just that — a *machine*. Machines will either perform flawlessly — usually in the hands of a skilled operator — or else poorly, as in the hands of an inexperienced person. It is commonly said that "It's a lousy mechanic who places the blame on his tools," and when it comes to operating a gold dredge, the same thing applies.

Running a gold dredge can either be sheer pleasure, or sheer *hell* if you don't know what you're doing. A lot of underwater prospectors will expect a dredge to do too much, and when their rig doesn't deliver what they expect of it, they are apt to become frustrated. Some dredgers will rant and rave, "My dredge doesn't move sixteen yards of gravel per hour like the spec sheet said it would! It won't pull from thirty-foot depths! It won't suck impacted gravel from crevices! All it does is plug up!" The list of complaints is endless, but in nine cases out of ten it is the *dredger's own fault* for not knowing the capabilities (*and* limitations) of his own equipment.

When a neophyte underwater prospector gets his hands on the intake nozzle (*or* tip) of a dredge, his first involuntary action will be to plunge the intake "full speed ahead" into the nearest patch of gravel and start suckin' away. All too often he is in for a rude awakening when he retracts the intake and finds that it is no longer sucking. A plug! Neophyte dredgers don't realize it, but they're making a big mistake when they haphazardly plunge the intake into gravel assuming it will be sucked up without difficulty. If you work a dredge with *this* idea in mind, you're going to face one plug-up after another.

In order to run a dredge free of plugging, consider Thornton's Rule Number Five: "Never blindly stick the intake of a dredge into gravel assuming it will automatically be sucked up; instead, place the intake within a few inches of the gravel and allow the vacuum to pull the gravel *toward* it." If you spot any rocks that look as though they're too large to negotiate the intake and suction hose, use your hands to move them away from the intake so they won't be sucked in. Keep a special eye out for long, thin rocks, particularly when using a suction nozzle type of dredge. When such a rock enters a suction nozzle and passes the orifice, the high-powered jet stream will occasionally flip the rock in such a manner that it will lodge edgewise inside the bent tubing.

And now for Thornton's Rule Number Six: "After sucking in gravel for five seconds or so, pull the intake away from the gravel and let plain water run through the system for a couple of seconds." By working the intake in this manner, the material you just sucked up will get a chance to move several feet up the suction hose before another surge of gravel comes along. Remember — the *more* the gravel is spread out over the length of the vacuum system, the *less* chance there is of getting a plug-up.

In spite of the aforementioned precautionary measures, a gold dredge will still plug up on occasion. An experienced operator can actually tell *where* in the system the plug is located, and thereby remove it quickly and with a minimum of effort. If you're not an experienced operator, then by gosh I'll *make* you one!

In any type of gold dredge (suction nozzle, power-jet, or circle-jet) there are two kinds of plug-ups — the intake of the dredge will either be completely (or almost completely) "dead" with little or no suction, or else a surge of water will be emerging from the intake. Memorize these rules: When there is *no suction whatsoever* (or perhaps very little), the plug is located at some point *ahead* of the orifice. If there is *water flowing from the intake*, the plug is located *behind* the orifice, and the water flowing through the system is hitting the obstruction and flowing backwards through the suction hose to pour out of the intake end.

In a suction nozzle type of rig, the most common plug-up point will be immediately behind the orifice where the rocks negotiate the bent section of tubing. A rock lodged here will cause a very powerful backwash to emerge from the intake of the nozzle, and you will immediately know where the trouble lies. A plug-up at this point is most easily removed by inserting a long, rigid object — a pry bar used for working crevices works nicely here—up into the nozzle. If the end of the pry bar succeeds in reaching the obstruction, a few good jabs should knock out the plug. (See Figure 50) If the end of the pry bar doesn't quite reach the plug, discontinue the jabbing — you *may* damage the wall of the suction nozzle and, in time, actually poke a hole through. Rather than take this chance, it is a better idea to disconnect the suction hose from the back of the nozzle and knock the plug out from that end. (These same procedures, incidentally, are also used for knocking plugs out of an underwater dredge, which also employs a suction nozzle. If you have such a dredge, it is a good idea to also carry a long, but lightweight metal rod for the purpose of knocking out plugs from the back end of the dredging tube which can't be reached from the front.)

If there is a water surge of *noticeably less velocity* emerging from the intake of a suction nozzle, this will signify that the plug is situated *well behind the orifice*, either in the suction hose or at the collar where the hose attaches to the back of the sluice box (see Figure 51). First try the suction hose. Pick up the nearest hand-sized rock and firmly rap the suction hose at regular intervals. (Don't worry about damaging the hose — it's designed to take a lot worse!) A plug in the suction hose usually will be removed by the impact of the rock, but if this doesn't work, try shaking the hose vigorously, followed by more rapping. This is sure to do the trick.

If you still have a plug at this point, the trouble may lie at the sluice box collar. If your sluice has a swing-open baffle box, open the baffle and visually inspect the collar. If there are rocks jammed inside the opening, you've located the source of your trouble. Give the rocks a good, hard knock and they will come out, allowing things to flow freely again. If your baffle box doesn't swing open, it will be best to kill the engine, unclamp the suction hose from the collar and make a hind-side inspection. The procedure for removing the plug is the same . . . knock it!

Of course, there is always the possibility of developing the simplest plug-up of all — the kind that is located ahead of the orifice, or, just barely inside the intake of the suction nozzle. In a case such as this you will get virtually no suction at all, because the vacuum created by the emerging jet stream is unable to draw in water through the intake. Your pry bar will again prove its versatility by knocking out this obstruction.

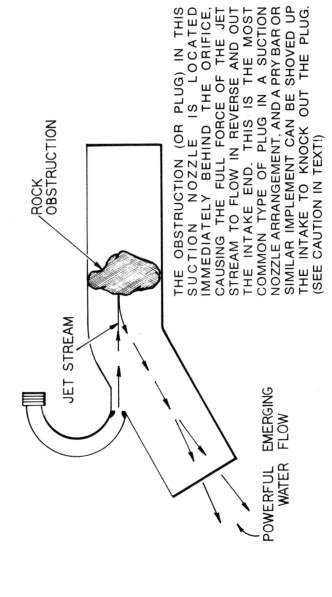

ROCK
OBSTRUCTION

JET STREAM

POWERFUL EMERGING
WATER FLOW

THE OBSTRUCTION (OR PLUG) IN THIS
SUCTION NOZZLE IS LOCATED
IMMEDIATELY BEHIND THE ORIFICE,
CAUSING THE FULL FORCE OF THE JET
STREAM TO FLOW IN REVERSE AND OUT
THE INTAKE END. THIS IS THE MOST
COMMON TYPE OF PLUG IN A SUCTION
NOZZLE ARRANGEMENT, AND A PRY BAR OR
SIMILAR IMPLEMENT CAN BE SHOVED UP
THE INTAKE TO KNOCK OUT THE PLUG.
(SEE CAUTION IN TEXT!)

Figure 50—The common "plug point" in a suction nozzle.

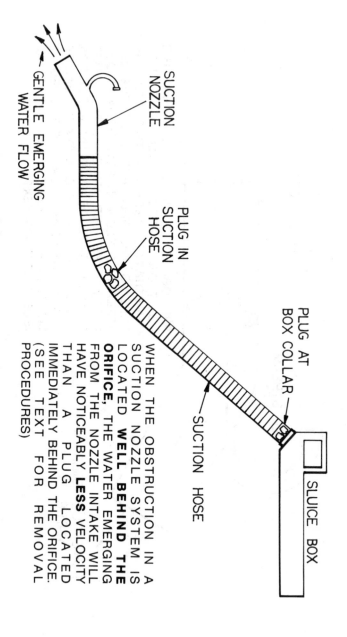

GENTLE EMERGING
WATER FLOW

SUCTION
NOZZLE

PLUG IN
SUCTION
HOSE

SUCTION HOSE

PLUG AT
BOX COLLAR

SLUICE BOX

WHEN THE OBSTRUCTION IN A SUCTION NOZZLE SYSTEM IS LOCATED **WELL BEHIND THE ORIFICE**, THE WATER EMERGING FROM THE NOZZLE INTAKE WILL HAVE NOTICEABLY **LESS** VELOCITY THAN A PLUG LOCATED IMMEDIATELY BEHIND THE ORIFICE. (SEE TEXT FOR REMOVAL PROCEDURES)

Figure 51—Diagram of obstructions in suction nozzle system, well behind the orifice.

The nearest thing to a "plug free" suction dredge is the type that employs a power-jet. In this aspect of the Venturi principle, there are no bent sections of tubing for the gravel to travel through, meaning fewer plug-ups from the very beginning. Except for when it is traveling through the suction hose, gravel has a "straight shot to the surface" when passing through a power-jet tube and will encounter little resistance. But still, there will always be that one rock out of a hundred that was just "born to be bad."

When a power-jet dredge plugs, the unwanted blockage will usually be in the actual power-jet tube itself. It doesn't matter if the plug is located at the beginning of the power-jet, in the middle, or at the end which connects to the collar of the sluice box — the procedure for removing all three types of jet-related plugs is the same.

If you are the owner of a power-jet dredge, you've probably expressed curiosity over the round, stoppered hole in the face of your sluice's baffle box. The same applies to the seemingly useless, long steel rod with a "T-handle" which came with your dredge. Actually, the technical name for that "useless" steel rod is a *probe rod*, and it is used for "running out" plugs in the power-jet tube. First, the probe rod is inserted into the hole in the face of the baffle box. (The stopper in the baffle box hole is merely to prevent a stream of water from shooting out when the dredge is running.) From there, the rod is run down through the baffle box, out the box collar, down the complete length of the power-jet tube, and out into the first few inches of suction hose. If there is a plug-up anywhere along the line — at the collar, near the orifice, or at the suction hose connection — a few nice, hard shoves on the probe rod will remove it. (See Figure 52) If for some reason the plug is *not* located in the power-jet tube, use the same methods as described for a suction nozzle rig to track down the blockage, which will either be in the suction hose or at the intake tip. As in the case of a suction nozzle, if the plug is located *ahead* of the orifice of the power-jet tube, you will have little or no suction. If the plug is *behind* the orifice, water will flow from your intake tip. Act accordingly.

When it actually comes time to dredge a gold-bearing deposit, you can use either of the two common methods of sinking your hole. First, you can make a "straight dive for the bottom," or else dredge a "lateral-spread" type of hole. Each has distinct advantages, but in most cases it's the lateral-spread hole that wins out.

When a dredger isn't quite sure about the nature of the bedrock underlying a deposit, or if he wishes to grab a fast sample of bedrock material without going through a lot of trouble, he will make a *straight dive for the bottom*. When making a "straight dive," a dredger will start mining at a location that shows good surface in-

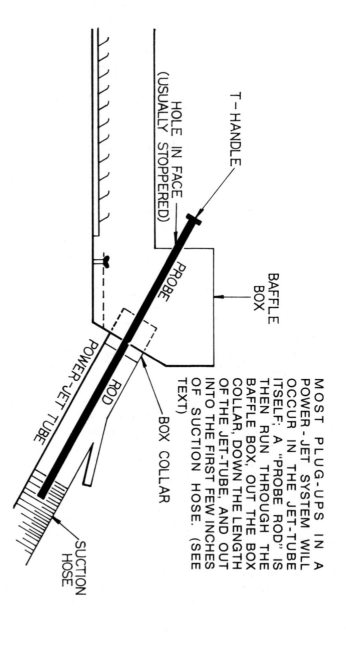

MOST PLUG-UPS IN A POWER-JET SYSTEM WILL OCCUR IN THE JET-TUBE ITSELF; A "PROBE ROD" IS THEN RUN THROUGH THE BAFFLE BOX, OUT THE BOX COLLAR, DOWN THE LENGTH OF THE JET-TUBE, AND OUT INTO THE FIRST FEW INCHES OF SUCTION HOSE. (SEE TEXT)

HOLE IN FACE (USUALLY STOPPERED)

T-HANDLE

BAFFLE BOX

PROBE

POWER-JET TUBE

ROD

BOX COLLAR

SUCTION HOSE

Figure 52—Probe rod path through power-jet eduction system.

dications and excavate a somewhat vertical, steep-sided hole that will lead him to bedrock with a minimum of time and effort. (Figure 53) Of course, when he finally *gets* to the bottom, he won't have any room to move around, as he'll only expose two or three square feet of bedrock at the most. But if the walls of the hole stay intact long enough without caving in (something which frequently happens, incidentally), the dredger can often get a good idea of what the bedrock holds and whether or not it warrants a large-scale operation. So in this sense, anyway, the straight dive for the bottom has its merits.

Really, though, to expose a large enough area of bedrock to make it worth your while requires the excavation of a *lateral-spread* hole. This type of hole is dredged in stages, starting out small and finally ending up with a monstrous excavation once bedrock is reached. There is little chance of a lateral-spread hole caving in on you, because the walls are gently sloping. Furthermore, the resulting gentle slope of the walls will make the removal of large boulders that much easier. (More on that a bit later.)

To get an idea of how a lateral-spread hole is excavated, let's study Figure 54. The first things you will notice are the letters A, B, C, D, E, F and G at the left-hand side of the illustration. These are the "stages of completion," starting out with A and ending with G.

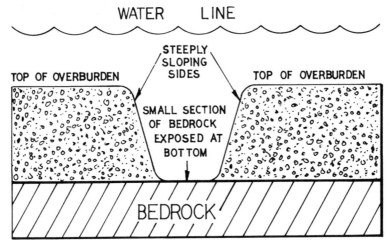

Figure 53—Diagram of a "straight dive for the bottom" type of hole.

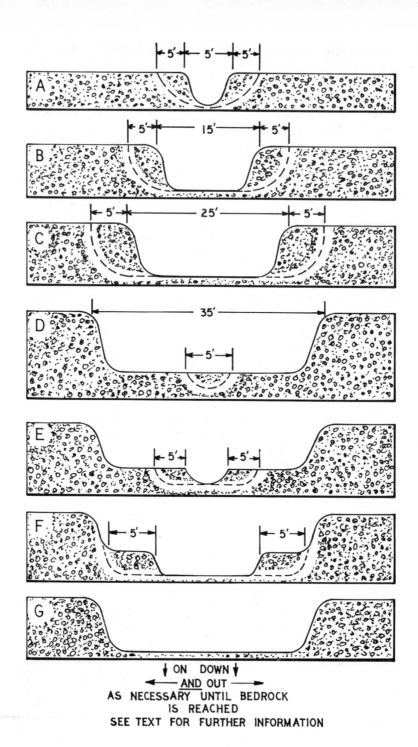

Figure 54—Diagram of a "lateral-spread" type of hole.

Actually, when dredging in a real river there can be more stages than illustrated here, going all the way to "Z" if so required.

Stage "A" at the top of the illustration portrays the initial hole that is started into the top of the overburden. In this hypothetical situation, let's say that the width of the initial hole—from crest to crest — is five feet. Notice the dashed lines that extend from the bottom of the initial hole out sideways until they slant upward to the top of the overburden. The gravel within these boundaries — let's make it five feet of space on both sides of the initial hole — is the *next* goal for you to attain with your dredge, and after you've extended the hole outward to these new boundaries you will now have a hole *fifteen feet wide* as shown in Stage "B."

From Stage "B" the hole is extended outward again, five more feet on each side, and we wind up with a hole *twenty-five* feet wide as shown in Stage "C." From Stage "C" the hole is extended another five feet on each side, and finally we end up with a colossal "super hole" *thirty-five feet wide* as shown in Stage "D." At this point the hole is wide enough for you to move around in to your heart's content, and you can now forget about width for a while and concentrate on dredging the hole deeper.

Notice in Stage "D" the dashed line extending downward from the bottom of the "pit." If you clean out this gravel with your dredge, you will have a hole of the shape illustrated in Stage "E." From here on the "hole within a hole" is dredged wider according to the now-familiar dashed lines, going on to Stages "F" and "G."

Depending upon how deep you have dredged the hole at each successive stage, by the time you get to Stage "G" you should have made your way through at least six to ten feet of overburden. Many times, this great a depth is sufficient enough to place you on bedrock, but there is always the chance of running into that one rare spot where the overburden is fifteen or even twenty feet thick. On the average, if you haven't reached bedrock after going through, say, ten feet of overburden, it may be a wise idea to again extend the hole *laterally* in order to eventually dredge it deeper.

It should be pointed out that the lateral-spread hole is best and most easily excavated with a surface or sub-surface type of dredge, and one of the larger capacity models at that. These dredges pull the gravel through a long length of suction hose, enabling the dredger to run his tailings well enough away from the hole site so that they won't get in his way. This is a 180-degree turnabout from an underwater dredge, in which the gravel passes through a sluice tube to exit some seven or eight feet behind the operator. Now don't get me wrong . . . it *is* possible to excavate a lateral-spread hole with an underwater dredge — there are many operators who do it — but you will have to constantly re-dredge your own tailings ever-backward as you widen the hole. In the end the results are the same, only when using an underwater dredge it will take much more time.

As you are working your way down through the overburden, you will encounter rocks of varying sizes. They will range from small, hand-sized rocks to full-fledged boulders three or four feet across and weighing several hundred pounds. These will have to be removed from the hole, but it is obvious that you can't pick up these monsters with your bare hands and toss them away.

Every dredger who has even the slightest intention of recovering gold uses a "come-along" and "boulder-sliding kit" to remove troublesome rocks from his hole. A "come-along" is a simple, lightweight hand-operated winch that is capable of lifting *two tons* of dead weight. The "boulder-sliding kit" consists of a special nylon webbing for wrapping around the unwanted boulder, a long length of quarter-inch steel cable (preferably 100 feet) which ties around some permanent object on shore for anchoring, and a cable gripper for taking up the slack in the line. All the necessary equipment for "pulling" boulders is shown in Figure 55.

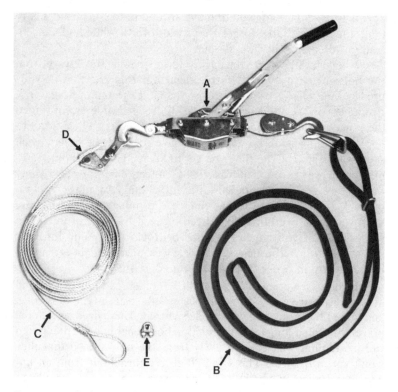

Figure 55—Any diver who has even the slightest intention of recovering "golden goodies" uses a come-along and boulder-sliding kit to remove troublesome boulders from his hole. The kit consists of four principal components — the come-along (A), boulder webbing (B), steel cable (C), and cable gripper (D). In case your steel cable doesn't have a tied-off loop on one end, you will also need a quarter-inch U-clamp (E). The proper methods of using boulder moving equipment can be found in the text.

In the vast majority of cases, boulder moving equipment is not used to lift large boulders from your hole, but rather to *pull* them out in a lateral motion. The gently sloping sides of a lateral-spread hole facilitate the removal of boulders, as you will find it easy to dredge a "boulder ramp" over which you can pull the unwanted rocks. A boulder ramp is simply a long, gently sloping surface which is dredged into one wall of your hole, slanting in the direction of the anchor point where the steel cable is attached. (Figure 56)

The first step in the successful use of boulder moving equipment involves the selection of a sturdy enough object on shore around which to secure your steel cable. Some boulders are very hesitant about sliding from their resting places, and a particularly stubborn one can actually pull the *anchoring object* from its hold once the steel cable is drawn tight. Try to tie your cable around the trunk of a nice, sturdy tree, at least a foot across. Any thinner than that and you're asking for trouble.

Tie your cable around the tree trunk at least *three times* to assure a good anchoring, and then thread it through the permanently tied-off loop which usually is supplied at one end of the cable. (Figure 57) Now run the cable out to your mining site while being careful to unravel any kinks or twisted spots; make certain the cable doesn't drag over any objects, as this can cause trouble once the winching process commences.

If your length of cable has no tied-off loop, you will need a quarter-inch "U-clamp" (refer to Figure 55) to secure the cable around the tree trunk. To start off, unscrew the two nuts on the U-clamp, remove the locking piece from the U-bolt, and set all these components in a safe place next to your tree so that they'll be handy. Next, wrap the cable around the tree trunk three times and place the short, remaining "free" end into the opened U-bolt together with the main length of cable. Replace the locking piece and tighten the nuts, making sure the clamp bites slightly into the cables. (Figure 58)

After the steel cable is stretched down to your mining site, it is time to wrap the nylon webbing around the boulder to be moved. Referring to Figure 59, you will notice that the webbing kit is composed of three pieces — the webbing itself, a "locking ring," and a thick piece of steel rod bent and welded into the shape of a triangle. Notice the two "arms" of webbing as shown in the illustration; in use, one arm is wrapped around the boulder in one direction, and the other arm as near perpendicular as possible to the first. When both arms are wrapped around the boulder, the "locking ring" is slid forward toward the boulder to prevent the webbing from slipping. The triangular piece that forms the dividing point for the two arm lengths is where the winching cable of the come-along is attached. (See Figure 60)

163

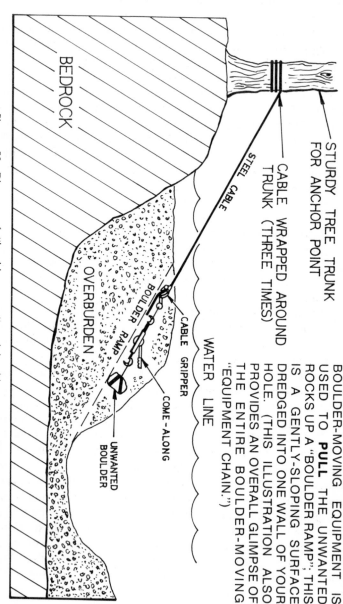

IN THE VAST MAJORITY OF CASES, BOULDER-MOVING EQUIPMENT IS USED TO **PULL** THE UNWANTED ROCKS UP A "BOULDER RAMP"; THIS IS A GENTLY-SLOPING SURFACE DREDGED INTO ONE WALL OF YOUR HOLE. (THIS ILLUSTRATION ALSO PROVIDES AN OVERALL GLIMPSE OF THE ENTIRE BOULDER-MOVING "EQUIPMENT CHAIN.")

STURDY TREE TRUNK FOR ANCHOR POINT

CABLE WRAPPED AROUND TRUNK (THREE TIMES)

STEEL CABLE

BEDROCK

OVERBURDEN

BOULDER RAMP

CABLE GRIPPER

COME - ALONG

UNWANTED BOULDER

WATER LINE

Figure 56—Diagram of "boulder ramp," and boulder-moving "equipment chain."

164

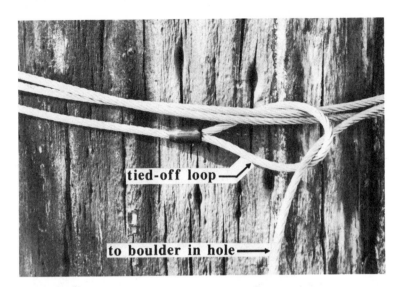

Figure 57—The length of steel cable that comes with a boulder-sliding kit usually has a permanently tied-off loop on one end. In use, the cable is wrapped around a sturdy tree trunk at least three times (a must!), and the free end is then threaded through the loop. From the tree, the cable goes down to the dredger's "hole," where the unwanted boulder is waiting to be removed.

Figure 58—If your length of steel cable doesn't have a tied-off loop on one end, you will need a quarter-inch "U-clamp" to secure your cable around the tree trunk. A U-clamp is a very inexpensive accessory item to the boulder-sliding kit, and you can purchase one at almost any hardware store. (See text for a complete description of the use of a U-clamp.)

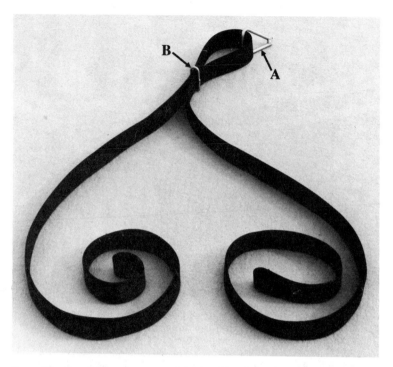

Figure 59—A very important part of the boulder-sliding kit is the special nylon webbing that is used to "lasso" the unwanted boulder. The triangular piece (A) is where the winching cable of the come-along is hooked onto the webbing; the locking ring (B) secures the webbing against the face of the boulder.

When the webbing is securely affixed to the unwanted boulder, release the ratchet wheel on the come-along and unravel the winching cable. Place the hook on the end of the winching cable into the "triangle" on the boulder webbing; now place the hook on the *opposite* end of the come-along into the eye on the "cable gripper." For the next procedure it is helpful to have a partner. Have your partner tug firmly on the steel cable which is attached to the tree on shore to take up the slack. When the cable is drawn as taut as possible, open the jaw of the cable gripper and slip the jaw over the steel cable. Slide the cable gripper (with the attached come-along and boulder webbing) up toward the tree as far as possible, and then let the jaw close; the excess cable will drop by the wayside, leaving a semi-taut, continuous "chain" of equipment running from the anchor point on the tree trunk all the way to the locking ring at the face of the boulder (refer back to Figure 56). You are now ready to start winching.

The first few pulls on the come-along's winching handle will do nothing except pull the "equipment chain" even tighter than before, but once the steel cable is perfectly taut, the boulder will start to slide from its resting place. Don't be disappointed when you find that each pull on the winching handle moves the boulder by only an inch or two; this is normal. After you have "reeled in" the entire length of the winching cable (usually six feet), you can use the "let-down lever" to release the tension on the cable system one notch at a time.

Since a come-along can pull boulders a maximum distance of only six feet during any one winching operation, you will have to repeat the process outlined in the preceding paragraphs as many times as necessary until the boulder is pulled up to the edge of your hole. Once there, you can usually roll it out of your way once and for all.

There are several other methods of removing boulders from a dredging spot. Some of the more professional dredgers working a permanent claim will construct a "derrick" or "log boom" which can be swung out over the dredging hole; a heavy-duty electrically operated winch with several hundred feet of thick cable is used in operations of this nature. The cable will extend up the length of the

Figure 60—In this photograph, we can see exactly how a boulder is "lassoed" with the nylon webbing of the boulder-sliding kit. One "arm" of the webbing is wrapped around the boulder in one direction, while the other arm is wrapped as near perpendicular as possible to the first. I should point out, however, that the webbing won't necessarily fit around your own boulder as it does in this example, which was, obviously, posed especially for this photograph.

boom to a pulley, and thereby down into the river. A special "sling" made of truck tire chains is used to lasso the boulder, and the powerful shore-mounted winch will lift it straight up and out of the hole. The boom is then swung aside to a dumping area where the boulder is dropped.

In rivers in which there is plenty of water clearance overhead, dredgers have been known to use fifty-five-gallon oil drums for the purpose of lifting boulders out of a hole. In practice, two drums usually will be strapped together and, by allowing water to leak in, sunk to the bottom of the hole. Again, a sling made of truck tire chains is used to secure the boulder, and the chains are then attached to the oil drums. Next, air from a surface compressor is pumped into the drums, and as the water inside is displaced, the drums will slowly start to rise toward the surface. Once the boulder is lifted high enough to clear the top of the overburden, the drums are carefully guided to a dumping area where the boulder is dropped.

Believe it or not, the electric winch found on the front fender of so many modern back-country vehicles can also be used to pull boulders. There are, however, two catches. First, you have to get your vehicle right down next to your dredging spot; second, the winch has to be powerful enough to "take it." And one more thing — *set your hand brake and prop blocks around your tires* so that you don't winch yourself into the river should the boulder decide to stay put!

In pages gone by I've covered such matters as positioning a dredge in a river, recognizing and alleviating plug-ups, working the intake nozzle in the correct manner, and so forth. But there are a few other matters that need to be discussed, and among these are the proper methods of tending a sluice box.

If there's one thing in particular that worries the neophyte gold-dredger, it's the accumulation of heavy material in the riffles of his sluice box. Time and time again, beginners will ask me, "How often should I clean out the concentrates in my sluice box? What should I do about the large rocks that lodge between the riffles? What's the best way to get the concentrates out of the sluice box and into my gold pan?" The list of questions is endless, and I'll try my best to come up with the answers that will help the greatest number of people.

Every river system is different, both in streamflow characteristics and in mineral content; the latter depends upon the type of rocks the river drainage flows over. All gold-bearing rivers of the Western United States contain a varying amount of black sand, which is derived from iron-bearing rocks. As I mentioned some time ago, there are *two types* of black sand — magnetic (called magnetite), and non-magnetic (known as hematite). The black sands that accumulate in the riffles of any gold-saving device are actually composed of a *mixture* of magnetite and hematite, and the ratio between the two will vary from river to river.

Magnetite black sand is extremely heavy, and if you're dredging in a river rich in this type of material, the current of water flowing through your sluice box will not be able to wash away very much of it. If this is the case, the underhang of the riffle bars will fill up rapidly and build up concentrate extending downward to the slant of the next riffle. *Never* let the riffles fill up to this stage, as there won't be any room for the necessary "eddy-currents" to form. A riffle of the type used in most sluice boxes is of the "Hungarian," or "Lazy L" design, and when the flow of water through the sluice box passes over such a riffle, an eddy-current is created on the underhanging side which causes heavy materials to settle into the "corner"; once here, they cannot escape. The lighter gravel components will circulate in the eddy-current and wash out, eventually finding their way out of the box entirely. This is the way a Hungarian riffle is *designed* to function, but if too much concentrate is allowed to accumulate, it *can't*. Thornton's Rule Number Seven: "A Hungarian riffle is operating at its best when the amount of accumulated black sand concentrate falls a little bit short of the midway point between each riffle bar." If the amount of black sand in your riffles necessitates a cleanup every couple of hours, by all means do it! (See Figures 61A and B, which illustrate a Hungarian riffle *and* a case of severe overloading, respectively.)

Of course, you may also be dredging in an area with a *low* percentage of magnetite but lots of hematite, which is less heavy; the flow of water through the sluice box will carry away much of the hematite, which will account for the large amount of black sand that will occasionally be found on your tailings pile. (This situation has shaken up more than one gold-dredger, who is apt to think that if the current carries away the black sand, it will *also* flush out the gold. There is no need to worry, because gold is infinitely heavier than hematite and will stay in the sluice box.) If hematite predominates over the heavier magnetite black sand in the river in which you're working, you'll be able to dredge for hours on end without your riffles filling to the "overflow" point. One cleanup at the end of each dredging day will be fine.

Occasionally, a large rock will settle in between the riffle bars of the sluice box, and when this happens, it is a good idea to "flick it" out into the current so that it will be carried away. When a rock settles in the riffles, the current flowing through the sluice box will create an eddy-motion around it which will cause all the concentrate in the immediate area of the rock to wash out of the riffle and travel further on down the box. This is a good job for the surface "safety man," who would otherwise stand around twiddling his thumbs

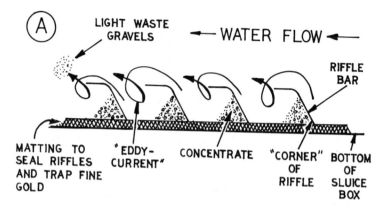

A "HUNGARIAN" RIFFLE SLANTS **WITH** THE FLOW OF THE WATER, CREATING AN "EDDY-CURRENT" ON THE UNDERHANGING SIDE. THIS EDDYING ACTION "BOILS" THE LIGHTER GRAVEL COMPONENTS OUT INTO THE WATER FLOW TO BE SWEPT AWAY, WHILE CONCENTRATING HEAVIER MATERIALS IN THE "CORNER" OF THE RIFFLE.

THESE RIFFLES ARE FILLED WITH TOO MUCH CONCENTRATE !

CONCENTRATE

NEVER LET YOUR RIFFLES FILL UP TO THE POINT WHERE THE CONCENTRATE EXTENDS DOWNWARD TO THE SLANT OF THE NEXT RIFFLE; THIS WILL INTERFERE WITH THE FORMATION OF THE NECESSARY "EDDY-CURRENTS."

Figure 61—Diagram of a Hungarian riffle *and* a case of riffle overloading.

while waiting for his turn at the nozzle to come up.

There are many methods of cleaning the concentrates out of a sluice box, and in my days I've seen some lulus. Some dredgers will lift the riffles of the sluice, hold their gold pan to the end of the box and scrape the concentrates into the pan with the edge of their hand. Others will do roughly the same by lifting the riffles, except they will splash water into the sluice to wash the concentrates into their pan. Others yet will roll up the matting that lines the bottom of the sluice and rinse it out in their gold pan, losing half their concentrate in the process. Let me say right now that each of these methods is WRONG!!!

Before you attempt to clean out the concentrates, it is wise to let plain water run through the sluice box for a few minutes at the end of your "shift." To do this, lay the intake of the dredge in a location where it won't pull in any additional gravel, and the clear water now running through the system will wash away any light material that is still in the sluice box. After the light waste material has been flushed out, kill the engine and make a careful inspection of the material in the riffles. Pay special attention to the first three or four riffles of the sluice box — nine times out of ten, any heavy gold will settle in the upper portion of the box and will rarely travel further than the first few riffles. If you spy any pieces of gold during the preliminary inspection, pick them out with a tweezers and place them in a sample bottle.

The first step in removing the concentrates is to lift the riffles of the sluice box by releasing the locking latches which usually are found at the discharge end of the box. Once the riffles are lifted and "flipped back" toward the baffle box, roll up the matting that lines the bottom of the sluice and thoroughly rinse it in a *deep bucket* so that no gold-bearing concentrate can escape. After rinsing the matting, hold the bucket to the end of the sluice box and use another bucket to splash water into the sluice to wash out the small amount of concentrate which will always adhere to the walls and bottom of the box. (These locations always yield values if any are present, particularly the bottom of the sluice; some of the finer pieces of gold will actually work their way *underneath* the matting that lines the bottom of the box.) Next, remove the classifier screen and flush out any gravel remaining inside the baffle box. When there is no material whatsoever remaining in the sluice box, you can safely consider it cleaned and proceed to the final step of the concentration process, panning.

The total cleanup of the sluice box will prove beneficial should you decide to move your dredge to another spot. If you *don't* thoroughly clean out your sluice box and you move to another area and start dredging there, the gold you find in the *new* spot may actually be gold remaining in the sluice from the previous location;

this may mislead you as to the presence of gold in the new area. A thorough cleanup of the sluice box before moving will insure that any gold found in the new area is *from* the new area!

Up to this point I have primarily discussed the operational practices of surface dredges. Those of you who plan on running underwater or sub-surface dredges may have justifiably felt slighted while reading the previous pages, but relax — now it's your turn!

The operational characteristics of an underwater dredge are entirely different from those of a surface rig because the underwater dredge is, in itself, different. A surface dredge is like a "component chain" — you have the gravel intake at the bottom of the river, the suction hose to deliver it to the surface, and the sluice box to process it. The underwater dredge, on the other hand, is an all-in-one unit — gravel is taken in at one end of the long metal dredging tube, pushed by the jet stream down the length of the tube, and finally over the riffle tray at the back end. It is no small wonder, then, why an underwater dredge differs so greatly from its surface bretherin.

One of the major obstacles encountered while operating an underwater dredge is the sheer size of the dredging tube itself. Frequently, the dredging tube will be six, seven, or even eight feet long, making it necessary to have a man working at both the front and back ends. In operation, the man working the intake end can give "hand signals" to the man at the rear, indicating when he wishes to move the dredging tube forward, backward, or off to one side. An underwater dredging tube is extremely heavy when full of gravel, rocks and water, and it *takes* two divers to handle one satisfactorily.

Few underwater dredgers realize it, but when they tilt the angle of the intake nozzle (for example, to get at a certain patch of gravel), they also tilt the entire length of the dredging tube behind them — including the riffle tray. This should be avoided at all cost, because once the riffle tray is tilted, the concentrates will spill over to one side of the tray and wash out. Always keep the dredging tube perfectly level, a task made all the easier by having a man working the back end. If the man at the intake end gets carried away and starts to tilt the dredging tube, the man in back can quickly force the tube back into level position and save the concentrates.

If it is necessary for you to run your underwater dredge in an area where currents are present (no matter how swift or gentle), position the rig so that the length of the dredging tube is *parallel* with the flow of the current. If you don't, the force of the current against the mass of the dredging tube will be too much for you, and keeping the tube level will prove to be fantastically difficult.

When it comes time for cleaning out the riffle tray of an underwater dredge, *don't* attempt to bring the entire dredging tube up to the surface of the stream — this will increase by a millionfold the chances of tilting the riffle tray and losing *everything*. Instead, position the dredging tube on a stable surface beneath the stream and simply remove the riffle tray itself. Carry it up to the surface, lift out the riffles, and rinse the matting in a bucket just as if you were cleaning a surface sluice box. The gold pan is once again the final stage of the recovery process.

Whatever you do, don't attempt to run an underwater dredge all day long without cleaning out the concentrates. Not only is it possible for the riffle tray to load up in a short time (this occurs when working in areas heavily laden with magnetite black sand), there's the ever-present danger of tilting the dredging tube. By cleaning the riffle tray every hour or so, you'll only lose an hour's worth of concentrate should you experience a major upset. But if you've been dredging steadily for hours on end (let's say from breakfast time until twelve noon) and *then* the dredging tube tilts on you, you've lost half a day's worth of concentrate!

The operation of a sub-surface dredge is very much like that of a surface rig, and yet there are overtones of the underwater dredge which peek through.

The sluice box of a sub-surface dredge is much larger than the riffle tray of an underwater dredging tube, allowing the sub-surface dredge to be run for hours without a cleanup. Also, the sub-surface dredge is easy to work with since all you have to maneuver underwater is the flexible suction hose and intake tip; there is no danger of tilting a sub-surface sluice box. But in spite of the ease of operation, remember one thing — since the sluice box of a sub-surface dredge is suspended from chains (or cables, whichever the case may be), the box is subject to battering from stream currents. As in the case of an underwater dredge, make sure that the sub-surface sluice box is parallel with the flow of any prevailing currents. It is also a good idea to suspend the sluice box several feet *above* the bottom of the river, so that the current has a chance to pick up the tailings and carry them away as they emerge from the discharge end. (The current of a stream always flows slower at the bottom of the channel and swifter at middle and upper depths, hence this advice.)

As far as the cleanup of a sub-surface dredge goes, follow the same procedures that are used for cleaning the riffle tray of an underwater dredge. In this case, however, you won't have to find a secure place on which to rest the sluice box — it is already suspended from the flotation rig in a stationary position, and removing the riffle tray will be an easy task. The *tray only* is brought up to the surface for a thorough cleaning by methods now familiar to you.

So there you have it — all the information necessary (lordy, I sure hope I've *covered* everything) for going out and using that shiny, new gold dredge to the best advantage. I'm utterly confident that I've managed to put down a great many of the common myths concerning gold-dredging, as well as bring to light a number of facts that otherwise would be obtained only through years of experience. I should, however, point out that the information offered here is by no means "All Mighty." In time, you will discover and nurture little tricks *of your own* which will eventually lead you to bigger and better gold discoveries. And really, isn't that what it's all about?

CHAPTER TWELVE

Amalgamation—The Art of Recovering Fine Gold

In the life of every gold-dredger, there comes the time when he will encounter gold particles so fantastically fine that he'll actually be afraid to pan his concentrates down to the pure metal, lest he lose any. Exactly what a dredger does with this tricky material from here on depends upon how long he's been engaged in the sport. A beginning dredger, for example, will meticulously attempt to pick out every single speck of gold with a tweezers. A dredger with a year or two of experience under his belt will wash his concentrates into a bucket to take home for eventual processing (that word "eventual" frequently turns into *never*). And then there's the seasoned, professional dredger — when *he* looks into a pan of concentrate and sees particles of "flour gold," he'll immediately wash the whole mess right back into the river because he knows that the small amount of gold he's throwing away simply *isn't worth* going through the hassle of recovering it. After all, when you're talking about gold so small that it takes, perhaps, a thousand particles to be worth *one cent* . . . well, you can see why I say it isn't worth it! Still, there are countless dredgers who insist on recovering every speck of flour gold in their concentrate, and the only way to get it all is by the process of *amalgamation.*

Amalgamation is a gold-recovery process that is thousands of years old, and involves the use of mercury (also known as "quicksilver") to pick up tiny particles of gold that are so frightfully easy to lose by other methods. The word "amalgamate" means to mix or blend, and mercury will do this when brought into contact with certain metals; gold, silver, copper, platinum, and zinc are among the more common metals which will amalgamate with mercury. One metal which will *not* amalgamate with mercury, however, is iron, and because of this fact, mercury can be mixed with black sand concentrates (which *are* largely iron) to assimilate all the gold that is present, while completely ignoring the black sand. The substance formed by the "marriage" of gold and mercury is called *amalgam,* which eventually is heated to drive off the mercury. At the end of the process, free, uncontaminated gold remains.

Much of the gold in black sand concentrates is considerably dirty, often being coated with iron stain, sulfides, limonite rust (limonite is a decomposed, non-magnetic form of iron), and sometimes a hard coating of dirt or clay as in the case of gold particles which recently washed down from high benches, old Tertiary channels, etc. Dirty gold *will not* amalgamate with mercury, and the first step of the amalgamation process is to clean the concentrates so that each and every gold particle can be assimilated.

The easiest and quickest way to clean black sand concentrates is to expose them to a substance which should now be very familiar to you, *nitric acid*; a plastic gold pan will also come in handy. Place the concentrate in the plastic pan, and spread it evenly over the entire bottom. Now cover the concentrate with about half an inch of water, and add concentrated nitric acid until a slight "boiling" action occurs; the mixture will boil when the ratio of acid-to-water reaches a concentration of approximately 10:1. Whatever you do, perform this step exactly as I described it here. NEVER pour acid into the pan first and then add water — this will cause the acid-water mixture to spatter violently, and severe burns will result should some of it splash onto you. Remember, always add *acid to water* — never the reverse!

If the gold in the concentrate is extremely dirty, you may find it advantageous to add straight acid to the black sand. In either case — diluted or straight — swirl the contents of the pan around for a couple of minutes to make sure all the material is completely exposed to the action of the acid. But don't get too carried away, as this will increase the danger of splashing. Once the concentrate has been cleaned and the nitric acid washed from your pan, it is time to add mercury to assimilate the gold.

Before I go any further, I must point out that mercury is a very dangerous substance if not handled properly. Particularly deadly are the *vapors* given off by mercury whenever it is removed from its container, and therefore you should avoid using the substance any longer than necessary. Mercury vapors, when taken into the body, have a habit of slowly (but *surely*) working their way into a person's brain, causing a gradual decomposition of the brain cells! Contrary to what you may have read elsewhere, mercury *does* give off vapor when exposed to normal air temperatures, in addition to when it is heated. Use mercury only out of doors where there is good ventilation; if you can't go outdoors, then don't use it at all! And if mercury vapors aren't bad enough, stay away from the stuff if you have any open sores or cuts on your hands — a tiny "bead" of mercury can get inside the body this way, too.

To determine the amount of mercury that is needed for proper amalgamation, you must "guesstimate" the amount of gold that is present in the concentrate; this may be difficult, but it is important. Generally speaking, use *twice as much* mercury as there is gold in the concentrate. You'll see why very shortly.

After mercury has been added to the pan of concentrate, the pan should be vigorously agitated — preferably under water. This causes the mercury to meander throughout the black sands for complete contact with all gold particles, no matter how minute. As the pan is agitated, the mercury will break up into hundreds of tiny globules and spread throughout the concentrate, picking up gold along the way. As gold is assimilated into the mercury, the globules will become stiff and lose their ability to roll along with the motion of the pan. This is normal, but if too little mercury was initially added to the concentrate, the globules will be unable to "puddle" and roll back into one large mass of mercury and gold at the end of the agitation process. This is why you should be generous with the mercury. By agitating the concentrate under water, the resulting amalgam mixture will puddle easier than if agitated out of water.

When the amalgam mixture has been puddled back into one large mass, the now-barren black sand is panned off; use the same careful panning motion as if you were panning concentrate down to the pure gold. If you see globules of amalgam working their way toward the surface, shake the pan a few times to work them back down to the main mass at the bottom of the pan. After you've panned off as much black sand as possible, pour the remaining amalgam mixture into a safe container.

The amalgam which now sets before you contains a considerable amount of excess mercury which must be removed before you can go any further. Perhaps the easiest and most efficient method of getting rid of excess mercury is to squeeze the amalgam mixture through a chamois skin. The free, unalloyed mercury will pass through the pores of the skin, but the particles of true amalgam will remain. A thin-skinned chamois is required for this process, as mercury cannot pass through the thicker skins.

Soak the chamois in water for a few minutes to make it soft and manageable, and then push the skin down into a deep, narrow vessel. Pour the amalgam mixture into the "pocket" that is formed, and bring together the portions of the chamois which are draped over the edges of the vessel. Lift the chamois from the vessel, being careful not to upset the amalgam in the pocket. Now place the entire chamois *under water* inside a large container, and start to twist the chamois so that the amalgam in the pocket is compressed. As the amalgam becomes more and more compacted, droplets of excess mercury will force their way through the chamois skin and out into the container. Particles of assimilated gold will not pass through the skin, because they are too large; they will remain in the pocket. The chamois is twisted under water so that if the skin ruptures, mercury will not shoot out all over the place — instead, it will be contained in the vessel by the cushioning effect of the water.

Continue to squeeze the chamois until no more mercury passes through the skin. Lift the chamois from the water, and squeeze it to drive off any remaining moisture. Open up the chamois, and there in front of your eyes will lay a hard, bright, silver-colored lump of gold amalgam, free of excess mercury. It is ready for the final stage of the amalgamation process, *retorting*.

To "retort" amalgam means to drive off the mercury by means of distillation. Mercury will readily vaporize at a temperature of 675 degrees Fahrenheit, whereas gold will stay solid until heated to about 1,945 degrees. The distillation of amalgam requires a specially constructed mercury retort, which can be purchased at the more sophisticated mining supply stores which deal primarily in commercial mining equipment.

The complete retort setup consists of three principal parts — a *heat source* (usually a portable propane gas torch), a *retorting vessel* for holding the amalgam, and a *condenser* for turning the mercury vapors back into liquid mercury for recovery and eventual re-use. Your mining supply dealer usually will carry the retorting vessel and condenser, and the propane torch can be purchased from just about any hardware store.

The retorting vessel itself is basically a steel pot, with a steel lid that is carefully machined to insure a tight fit. The lid usually will have a turn-screw clamp, which tightens the seal even more. A metal pipe exits from the lid of the retorting vessel, and is bent downward on an angle to run into the condenser. The condenser is a long length of tubing surrounded by a "water jacket." The condenser has two openings in the jacket, one at the lower end and another at the upper end. Cold water is run through a hose into the *lower* end of the condenser assembly, and it travels up the jacket to exit at the upper end. As hot mercury vapors emerge from the retorting vessel and enter the condenser, the cold water flowing through the jacket and *against* the inside tubing causes the vapors to "condense" back into liquid mercury. The mercury then leaves the condenser and enters the outlet pipe, which leads to a collecting vessel filled with cold water. (See Figure 62)

Occasionally, mercury vapors will not completely condense inside the inner tubing of the condenser assembly, and for this reason the end of the outlet pipe is placed *under water* inside the collecting vessel. In case any vapors emerge from the outlet pipe in an uncondensed state, the cold water in the collecting vessel will complete the task. It is extremely important that you place the end of the outlet pipe JUST BARELY under water in the collecting vessel. Here's why. After the retorting process is completed (I'll get to the full details in a bit), the retorting vessel is allowed to cool, and as it does a vacuum is created in the latter which frequently draws water from the collecting vessel up the outlet pipe and into the condenser. This in itself is not particularly harmful, but if you place the outlet pipe *well beneath the water* in the collecting vessel, the vacuum created by the cooling retorting vessel will draw water all the way up into that container, where it may turn into steam and cause an explosion. It is for this reason why many prospectors tie a wet cloth around the end of their condenser outlet pipe to form sort of a "conduit" which guides the emerging mercury down below the water line; when doing this, the actual end of the outlet pipe remains just a "hair" out of the water.

Because of the possibility of leaks in the network of pipes and tubing, it is extremely important that you set up your retorting equipment OUT OF DOORS; too many people have died from mercury poisoning while trying to retort amalgam in their homes. The large quantity of mercury vapor released by heating is *ruthless*, and can kill you before you can get outside into the fresh air.

After the retorting apparatus is set up, it is wise to coat the inside of the retorting vessel with a thin film of chalk or graphite — this will prevent the gold from sticking to the bare metal once the mercury has been driven off. Always let the coating dry thoroughly before adding the amalgam. To further protect against the possibility of sticking, some prospectors also line the inside of their retorting vessel with a double thickness of newspaper.

When you load the amalgam in the retorting vessel (also known as "adding the charge"), add it in the form of small lumps not over an inch in diameter. Make sure that you never load the vessel more than half full. Amalgam *expands* as it is heated, and if the vessel is loaded too full, the charge may swell up toward the top of the vessel and block off the vapor outlet, causing the retorting vessel to explode.

Once the charge has been added, screw down the lid of the retorting vessel as tight as possible. To prevent leakage of deadly

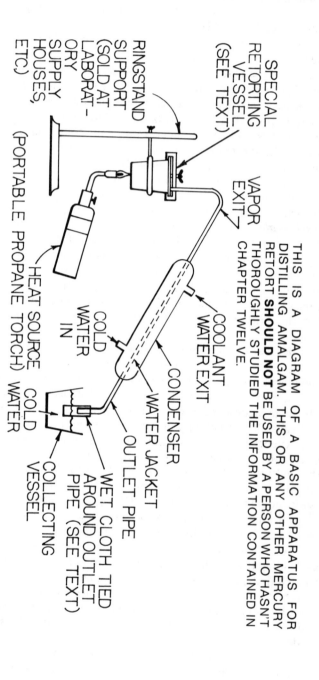

THIS IS A DIAGRAM OF A BASIC APPARATUS FOR DISTILLING AMALGAM. THIS OR ANY OTHER MERCURY RETORT **SHOULD NOT** BE USED BY A PERSON WHO HASN'T THOROUGHLY STUDIED THE INFORMATION CONTAINED IN CHAPTER TWELVE.

SPECIAL RETORTING VESSEL (SEE TEXT)

RINGSTAND SUPPORT (SOLD AT LABORATORY SUPPLY HOUSES, ETC)

VAPOR EXIT

HEAT SOURCE (PORTABLE PROPANE TORCH)

COOLANT WATER EXIT

COLD WATER IN

CONDENSER WATER JACKET

OUTLET PIPE

COLD WATER

WET CLOTH TIED AROUND OUTLET PIPE (SEE TEXT)

COLLECTING VESSEL

Figure 62—Diagram of a mercury retorting apparatus.

mercury vapors, seal the vapor pipe connection and "lid crack" with a generous amount of wet clay. You are now ready to commence the actual retorting operation.

Turn on the flow of cold water through the condenser, and fire up the heat source. It is important that you heat the retorting vessel *gradually* at first, so that the iron vessel just starts to glow a dark red. As the temperature in the vessel approaches 675 degrees Fahrenheit, the mercury contained in the amalgam will vaporize, and you will soon notice a steady trickle of liquid mercury pouring from the end of the condenser outlet pipe. Whatever you do, don't be hasty about "pouring on the heat." If you heat the amalgam too quickly, the mercury may boil and throw bits of amalgam up toward the top of the retorting vessel, to possibly plug up the vapor outlet and cause an explosion.

Once you see that no more mercury is pouring from the condenser outlet pipe, increase the heat for a few minutes so that the retorting vessel glows a bright red — this will drive the last bit of mercury from the amalgam. But don't keep the retorting vessel this hot for too long, or else the vessel may bulge outward. If it takes two or three hours to complete the entire retorting process, then *that's what it takes* — don't rush it!

After the last of the mercury has been driven off, turn off the heat and allow the retorting vessel to cool. When the vessel is cool to the touch, remove the lid and feast your eyes upon the gold in the bottom. Gold which is the end product of the retorting process is irregular in shape, and is covered with pock marks. Such gold is commonly referred to as "sponge gold."

Gold which has gone through the distillation/retorting process has *not* been purified, as is commonly believed. For example, if you place amalgamated .900 fine gold into a retort, you will still have .900 fine gold left after the mercury has been distilled away; any impurities in the gold itself will remain behind.

The distillation of amalgam in a retort is not the only means of separating gold from mercury. For the amateur prospector-dredger, there are two simple methods that yield the same results. These are the "baked potato" method, and the "long-handled shovel" method. Like the retorting process, both *must* be performed out of doors.

The "baked potato" method is commonly used to treat small quantities of amalgam which don't justify the trouble of setting up a retorting apparatus. This method is simple, practical, and really quite ingenious. What's more, it is very easily performed right in the field. Here's how it works. . . .

A large, well-rounded potato is cut in half, and a cavity just large enough to hold the amalgam is carved into one of the halves. (Figure 63) The amalgam is placed in the cavity, and the two halves

181

Figure 63—This is how your potato should look after you have sliced it and carved a cavity into one of the halves, for the purpose of holding your amalgam. (To illustrate the point, I've placed a bit of plain mercury inside this particular potato.) Make certain the potato you use for this process has enough good flesh to fully absorb the mercury vapors.

are butted back together and secured with wire. The potato is then wrapped in several layers of aluminum foil, and placed in the hot coals of a campfire to "bake." About one hour later (depending upon the size of the potato and the amount of amalgam), the heat of the coals will have vaporized the mercury and driven it into the flesh of the potato, leaving the gold in a free state inside the cavity. After the gold is removed, the potato is thoroughly crushed — then panned — by conventional methods to recover the mercury.

There are two precautions which must be taken when employing the baked potato method. First, since mercury is a deadly poison, DO NOT EAT THE POTATO! Second, don't sit too close to the campfire when baking your mercury-laden potato — the extreme heat of the coals will occasionally cause a potato to explode. While the thought of an "exploding potato" may, indeed, seem comical at first, try and tell that to the guy who just had red-hot amalgam spattered all over him!

The "long-handled shovel" method of treating amalgam is an offshoot of the baked-potato method, and is a bit simpler in nature. This method can be used whenever you find yourself short of "baling wire" and aluminum foil, which are required when using the baked-potato method. (I'll automatically assume that *every* prospector-dredger has a long-handled shovel!) The only negative point about the long-handled shovel method is that you will lose a small amount of your mercury through evaporation, unless you happen to have something with which to lute the edges of the potato.

To use the long-handled shovel method, start by slicing a potato in two and carving a cavity into one of the halves, the same initial procedure that's used in the baked-potato method. In this case, however, you won't need the other half of the potato, and you can "chuck it." Next, place your ball of amalgam on the blade of a long-handled shovel, and set the hollowed-out cavity of the potato half *over* the amalgam ball. Now arrange any rocks that are handy in such a manner that they will act as a "prop" by holding the blade of the shovel over the flames of an open campfire. (See Figure 64)

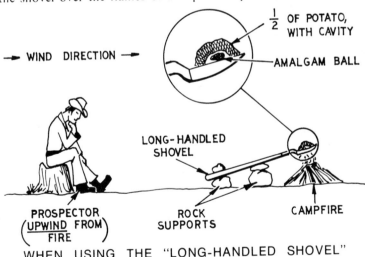

WIND DIRECTION

$\frac{1}{2}$ OF POTATO, WITH CAVITY

AMALGAM BALL

LONG-HANDLED SHOVEL

PROSPECTOR (UPWIND FROM FIRE)

ROCK SUPPORTS

CAMPFIRE

WHEN USING THE "LONG-HANDLED SHOVEL" METHOD TO TREAT YOUR AMALGAM, MAKE SURE YOU POSITION YOURSELF **WELL UPWIND** FROM THE CAMPFIRE!

Figure 64—The "long-handled shovel" method of treating amalgam.

Once the shovel blade is over the fire, the intense heat will vaporize the mercury and drive it into the flesh of the potato. Whatever you do, position yourself well away and UPWIND from the campfire — in case any mercury vapors escape from the potato, they will blow away from you. If the heat of the flames starts to turn your shovel blade a bright red, re-arrange your "rock pile prop" so that the blade isn't quite over the hottest part of the fire. To insure that all the mercury has been driven into the potato, allow the same period of "cooking time" that is used for the baked-potato method (approximately one hour). After enough time has elapsed, remove the shovel blade from the fire and allow it to cool; now lift the potato from the blade and feast your eyes upon your gold. The potato can now be crushed and panned to retrieve most of your mercury.

When processing *very small* amounts of amalgam, first recover as much of the excess mercury as possible by squeezing the amalgam in a chamois skin as described earlier. Now place the remaining amalgam in a plastic gold pan and add just enough concentrated nitric acid to cover it. Swirl the pan around for a few seconds, and in no time at all the mercury will be "dissolved away" by the acid, leaving bright, shiny gold.

Whenever mercury is reclaimed and re-used again and again, a film of dirt will eventually accumulate on its surface, making amalgamation difficult. You can recognize dirty mercury immediately because it will break up into many tiny balls and re-puddle with great difficulty. When the mercury reaches this stage, it must be cleaned before another amalgamation is attempted. Mercury is commonly cleaned by squeezing it through a chamois, or by agitating it in a 30:1 dilution of nitric acid and water. Either process will give mercury a new lease on life, and once again it will be ready to serve you. There is practically no limit to the number of times mercury can be cleaned and re-used.

In summing up, I would like to point out that amalgamation is a technique that should be used (1) when you have an extremely large amount of black sand concentrate to process; (2) when the gold *in* your black sand concentrate is microscopically fine; or (3) when every conceivable method of hand extraction has failed. Fine placer gold that has undergone the amalgamation process is never as attractive in appearance (nor as valuable) as gold which was hand-extracted from one's black sand concentrate. I would strongly advise you to thoroughly master the art of panning your black sand all the way down to the pure gold. This may sound like a lot of work, but the day may come when you will be happy you took the trouble. Clean, non-amalgamated fine placer gold can bring delightfully high prices because of "specimen value," which you can read about later on in Chapter Fifteen.

CHAPTER THIRTEEN

Nugget-Hunting with a Metal Detector— The Facts and the Fallacies

In the past few years, a great deal has been said about the importance of using the electronic metal detector in conjunction with a suction dredge to locate deposits of placer gold. Stories about how some guy "waves the search coil of his detector over the bottom of a stream and finds a pocket of gold-bearing black sand" are fairly common nowadays, and while a few of them are true, the vast majority are highly dubious. I personally feel that the prospecting public has been led astray by certain metal detector manufacturers (I won't mention any names, obviously) concerning the use of a metal detector in dredging applications, and in this Chapter I'm going to tell you — in language that leaves no doubts — *why* this is true. Now don't get me wrong. I'm *not* saying that a metal detector has no use in gold prospecting — it does, but not in gold *dredging!*

In this Chapter, I will discuss what types of metal detectors are best for the sport of "nugget-shooting," how they should be tuned, what a metal detector will (and *won't*) do as far as picking up gold, and much more. I can tell you right now that many of the facts in the following pages are completely contradictory to anything you've read before and are *sure* to raise the eyebrows of several so-called "personalities" of the prospecting/treasure hunting fields.

Too many people have the impression that the search coil of a metal detector is scanned over the bottom of a stream bed ahead of a suction dredge's intake, so that when the detector goes "Oooheee," the intake can be moved to that one spot to suck up the black sand and gold. This is the first myth (of many, I might add) to be torpedoed. In the first place, the search coil of the detector is far more likely to pick up the metal in the intake nozzle than it is any black sand. Second, black sand is far more prevalent toward the bedrock of a stream than near the surface; unless bedrock is very shallow and lying under perhaps six inches of overburden, the average metal detector won't even scan deep enough to pick it up! If bedrock should turn out to be buried under *five or six feet* of overburden as is commonly the case, you can safely leave your metal detector on the shore and stick to your dredge.

Perhaps the most flagrant violation of metal detector operational theory is that which instructs the prospector to search for gold with his detector turned to the "mineral" setting. In case you don't know what "mineral" means, it is that setting on a conventional, "first generation" metal detector which makes the unit sensitive to *ferrous* metal objects, namely those that contain a goodly percentage of magnetic iron; when tuned to this setting, a detector will pick up black sand and the gold that is sometimes found with it. Now, I agree with this part one hundred per cent, but as soon as you attempt to use your detector in a mountain streamflow environment, you're in for a rude awakening.

When a conventional metal detector is tuned for "mineral," it will respond to the most insignificant rock or pebble with a trace of iron mineralization in it. In fact, most gravel deposits found adjacent to Western gold streams are so heavily laden with "background" iron, the detector will go crazy as soon as the search coil is placed within a few inches of the ground! Unless you happen to have "X-ray vision" to make a sub-surface inspection of the object in question, it is impossible to tell whether the detector is picking up a mineralized pebble or an actual deposit of gold-bearing black sand.

Because conventional metal detectors work so unfaithfully when tuned for mineral (in a river environment, anyway), it will be necessary to tune the instrument to the opposite setting on the tuning knob, that which says "metal." By tuning for metal you are making the detector sensitive to *non-ferrous* metal objects, such as gold. When a detector is tuned for metal, iron mineralization will be tuned out to a certain degree, depending upon the sophistication of your particular instrument.

When going after placer gold, it is extremely important that you use a detector of great *sensitivity*, because gold is a difficult metal to detect. Just about any other metallic substance (with a few exceptions) "oxidizes" when buried in the ground for any length of time; the "zone of oxidation" consists of metallic ions which are leached off the metal by continued exposure to moisture in the earth. When detecting conventional metals such as silver, copper, iron, etc., the detector is greatly aided in its search by these zones of oxidation, which often extend several inches outward from the metallic object. When this occurs, an object that is buried, say, *six inches* in the ground will cause a detector to sound off louder and stronger than an object buried at *three inches* with little or no oxidation. Gold, however, is one of the Noble Metals, and does not leach, bleach, oxidize, or corrode. When you are using a metal detector to locate gold, you are reading off the bare, unoxidized metal itself, making it necessary to use an instrument with substantial depth potential and sensitivity.

I do not pretend to be an expert on the intricate electronic workings of metal detectors, but through personal experience I *do* know which detectors work best for a given application. There are two basic types of electronic metal detector — transmitter-receiver and beat frequency oscillator. Either type — TR or BFO — will detect metallic objects such as coins, rings, artifacts, etc., with satisfying results, but when it comes to placer gold, that's another story altogether. As far as "nugget-shooting" goes, the latest innovation in transmitter-receiver (TR) technology has a definite edge. This is the new "VLF" very low frequency detector.

Contrary to what you may have heard or read elsewhere, a VLF detector is not a new "type" of instrument. Simply stated, it is a redesigned transmitter-receiver detector that operates on a much lower frequency than earlier, first-generation TR units. The lower the operating frequency, the lesser the amount of search coil signal that is lost through "ground absorption"; this results in depth potential far exceeding BFO detectors. Also, thanks to some highly ingenious electrical engineering, the VLF detector is able to completely "tune out" troublesome, mineralized soil.

Whereas conventional TR detectors have a single, two-direction tuning knob for "metal" or "mineral," the new VLF models have *two* tuning knobs; one knob is an "air tuner," while the other is a "ground tuner." In practice, each VLF tuning knob is used in conjunction with the other to obtain a balance in the detection circuitry for whatever type of soil the instrument is being operated over. This can be done even over soil heavily laden with black, magnetic sand. Once a VLF detector is balanced for prevailing soil conditions, it will detect any and all metallic objects that generate a reflected signal *different* than the soil it was originally tuned to. This includes *both* ferrous and non-ferrous metals. If this sounds like something of a disadvantage, don't worry — most new VLF detectors also have built-in "discrimination" to give you a means of determining what lies below. Whenever your detector sounds off over a target in the VLF mode, you can usually flick a switch and go into "discriminate" and make a more precise definition of the target.

I would have to be an electrical engineer to explain the technical reasons for the foregoing operational characteristics, but unfortunately I am not. What's important, though, is that you *know* this information — only that way will you be able to select the type of metal detector that is best suited for nugget-shooting. And that's *definitely* a VLF transmitter-receiver!

Of all the information that has been published on nugget-shooting in the past, I have yet to find mention of factual principles that relate to the detection of placer gold according to its size. Detector manufacturers have long ballyhooed the ability of their instruments to detect pieces of gold "as small as rice grains," etc., all the way up to nuggets as large as your fist. While any detector will do the latter, very few will do the former. Too many people have the wrong impression about what a metal detector can do as far as locating gold, and that's my next subject.

The statement you're about to read may sound hard to believe, but it is true. . . . "A metal detector will respond to a solid, mass concentration of gold *better* than an equivalent weight in gold of smaller particles." Basically what I'm saying is this — if you place an ounce of loose, "flake" gold and a one-ounce gold nugget side by side and test them, a metal detector will react poorly to the flake gold while going "Zowie" over the nugget. To dramatize this statement, let me tell you of a little experiment I performed using a detector of the type commonly used for nugget-shooting. I even used a small three-inch search coil which is particularly suited for seeking out small objects like nuggets. (The diameter of a search coil determines the size of the objects you can detect; I'll get to this in a little while.) But for now, here's what I did. . . .

I started out with two plastic gold pans of equal size (ten inches wide) and placed them on a non-metallic surface. In one gold pan, I placed a half pound (six ounces) of loose, flake-type gold and shook it all into one corner of the pan to create as much mass as possible; in the other pan I placed a solid, one pennyweight gold nugget, and did it ever look measly in comparison! Next, I carefully tuned the detector — a transmitter-receiver type — to the metal side and waved the search coil over the one pennyweight nugget. At a height of two inches above the nugget I got my first reading, and at a height of one inch the detector screamed like a banshee.

Now I tried detecting the half pound of loose gold, which weighed *120 times as much* as the one pennyweight nugget. I placed the search coil three inches above the gold, and heard nothing. Two inches, and nothing. The same applied at a height of one inch. I then went to the extreme and placed the bottom of the search coil directly on top of the half pound of gold, and finally I got a reading (and a meager one, at that). I simply couldn't believe the results of this experiment, and I've since given up trying to explain it.

What it all adds up to is this — if a metal detector responds poorly to a huge accumulation of loose gold in one exact spot, how do you imagine it will react to flakes of gold spread out through a gravel deposit or crevice? The answer is, it won't! On the other hand, if there is a *solid nugget* of any mentionable size at all — even if it weighs only a few pennyweights — it will trigger the detector with little difficulty. If bedrock crevices full of flake gold are what you're searching for, you can always use a conventional non-VLF detector on the "mineral" setting to seek out telltale black sand; but as I stated previously, the background mineralization will drive you crazy. I can safely state that by and large, most prospectors who use a metal detector to look for gold search only for the larger nuggets which easily give themselves away by means of their mass metallic content.

Most of you are probably familiar with certain "convenience" features of metal detectors such as telescoping shafts, indicating meters, padded stereo headphones, and the like. While knowledge of these features is helpful, you can't really choose a good nugget-shooting detector until you understand that one *very* important characteristic, the diameter of the search coil.

Any good metal detector will feature interchangeable, *waterproofed* search coils, because a coil that's good for one application (coinshooting, for example) may not be good for another. (If you're going nugget-shooting around streams, waterproofed coils are a *must!*) Most metal detectors come ready-equipped with a search coil anywhere from six to eight inches wide, which is quite satisfactory for detecting medium-sized objects at medium depths. Large search coils (ten inches on up) are used for detecting large objects suspected of being buried at great depths, while the smallest detector coils (three to five inches) are hot for small objects a couple of inches below the ground. Here's an easier way to think of it. . . . *Large* search coil, large objects, great depths; *medium* search coil, medium objects, medium depths; *small* search coil, small objects, very shallow depths. It should, however, be pointed out that there are variables. It would be possible to detect a medium-sized object, for example, with a *large* search coil at a great depth, if that object has built up an exceedingly good oxidation zone. Likewise it is possible for a small three-inch coil to detect a large object close to the surface. Depth and pickup characteristics for metal detector coils will vary from one case to another, but on the whole the information presented here is factual.

While the chances of finding a large, fist-sized gold nugget are definitely there, you are far more likely to encounter nuggets that are considerably smaller. For nugget-shooting, it is recommended that you select either a three-inch or five-inch search coil for use with your detector, as these sizes are more likely to pick up smaller pieces of gold. This is not to say that a larger coil won't pick up small nuggets, but if the nugget is *very* small, detection will be difficult. Small search coils are ideal for getting into places where nuggets·are likely to occur, such as fissures in exposed bedrock, tangled tree roots at river's edge, or tight spots in between piles of boulders. A large coil would actually be a hindrance in such locations, and you'd only be able to detect in open areas which gold seldom favors with its presence. Be sure to study the section of photographs which you'll find at the end of this Chapter — these photos illustrate many types of conditions which are prime locations for profitable nugget-shooting!

The modern metal detector, just like autos off the assembly line, comes in a variety of body styles; the two most common are the "rod-mount" and "body-mount" configurations. The rod-mount detector is the most popular, and consists of the search coil, a long shaft (usually extendable) over which the conductor cable is wound, and the electronic control box. In this style of detector, the weight of the search coil at one end of the shaft is *counterbalanced* by the weight of the control box at the other. (Figure 65)

A detector that is rapidly gaining in popularity — particularly among nugget-shooters — is the body-mount unit. In this arrangement, the control box is mounted onto the upper portion of the operator's body by means of chest straps — the search coil attaches to the end of a plain, telescoping shaft which is highly maneuverable. Search coils designed for use with body-mount detectors often come with an extra foot or so of conductor cable so that the shaft can be maneuvered freely without tugging on the control box. (Figure 66)

The body-mount detector is praised by nugget-shooters because the shaft and search coil can easily be maneuvered without having to contend with the weight of the control box at the same time. It is very common for a prospector to attach a small nugget-shooting search coil to the end of the shaft and check out a variety of likely areas — including those which are located several feet *above* ground level. Good examples of this, in case you didn't know it, are fissures and "knotholes" in tree trunks along side a stream, which are often underwater during periods of extreme flooding. The weight of a body-mount shaft is very minimal, making it a simple matter to lift the shaft above your head to check such locations. Deposits of elevated "bench gravel" also become prey to the prospector using a body-mount detector, and occasionally a lucky nugget-shooter will locate a large nugget in such a spot.

The body-mount detector seems to be the all-'round, ideal detector for nugget-shooting, but I must point out that it is most easily operated when using a small, lightweight search coil (three to

Figure 65 — This is an example of a rod-mount style of metal detector. In this arrangement, the weight of the search coil is counterbalanced by the weight of the electronic control box at the opposite end of the shaft. This nugget-shooter is using a Fisher M-Scope Model 443, one of the many exciting "VLF" detectors currently on the market. This author has tested the numerous VLF detectors that have appeared since the initial printing of "Dredging for Gold . . . ," and the Model 443 seems to fulfill the need for a topflight, nugget-shooting detector.

Figure 66—This is a body-mount style of metal detector. The electronic control box is strapped onto the operator's chest, while the user maneuvers only the lightweight telescoping shaft and search coil. This style of detector is desirable for nugget-shooting applications, but it is not usually preferred for general use due to the fact that there is no control box at the end of the shaft to counter-balance the weight of the medium to large-sized search coils commonly used for coin-shooting, treasure-hunting, etc.

five inches). As you increase the size of the search coil you are also increasing the weight at the end of the shaft, only in this case there is no control box at the opposite end to *counterbalance* the weight of the coil. Unless the muscles of your arm are well developed, operating a body-mount detector with a large search coil can become very tiring after a while. This is where the rod-mount detector shines — and, believe it or not, many nugget-shooters have *both* styles. The decision of whether to purchase a rod-mount detector or a body-mount unit is a difficult one, and you will have to make it yourself. I hope I've presented enough information to allow you to make an intelligent choice.

No discussion on metal detectors would be complete without bringing up the subject of tuning techniques. On the whole, detector manufacturers give concise, down-to-earth recommendations for operating their units, but as far as nugget-shooting goes . . . well, I'd like to throw in a few hints of my own. The following tuning techniques apply to first-generation, non-VLF metal detectors *only.*

To start off, always turn the volume control of your detector on full blast and *leave* it there. This will insure that the speaker is delivering the loudest tone possible when the search coil passes over metal. As far as actual tuning goes, place the bottom of the search coil on the surface of the ground; turn the tuning knob toward the *metal side* so that when the search coil is lifted two inches off the ground, the detector's speaker will sound off. The detector is now tuned for the area in which you are working. In practice, move the search coil right on the surface of the ground, as this enables the coil's "lines of flux" to penetrate the ground as deeply as possible. If your instrument is correctly tuned, your speaker will sound off only when passing over a metal object. Don't lift the coil above the two-inch "tuning point" — this will cause the detector to give a false reading.

If, while detecting, you get faint, random buzzing sounds from the speaker while maneuvering the search coil between boulders, over bedrock, etc., you are working an area where the mineralization is so extreme it is actually "leaking over" into the metal tuning range. If you are using a transmitter-receiver detector, there is something you can do about this — if you're working with a BFO unit, there is not much you can do except trade it in for a TR!

If mineralized ground is "bugging" you, the first step is to find a boulder (or section of bedrock) that is representative of the background mineralization of the area. Next, place the search coil directly on such a surface and let the unit buzz away. Now turn the tuning knob *away* from the previously adjusted tuning point until the buzzing stops. Your detector is now tuned so that the background mineralization is partially neutralized, and you can maneuver your search coil a bit more freely than before.

The foregoing tuning tips *do not* apply to the newer VLF detectors. If you own one of these new instruments, I'd suggest that you follow the individual manufacturer's tuning instructions very carefully. I should emphasize that the more you use your new VLF detector, the more proficient you will become with it.

Another subject I must bring up is that of underwater metal detecting. Actually, the only parts of a metal detector that get placed underwater are the search coil and shaft, unless you've built some sort of waterproofed housing to accommodate the electronic control box. Ordinarily, the shaft can be submerged right up to the point where the conducting cable plugs into the control box.

Water temperature does crazy things to a detector's search coil, and as soon as you place your coil beneath the surface of a stream you're playing in a whole new ballpark. The detector usually will have to be retuned from scratch, because cold water frequently changes any tuning that was preset on land. There are no special techniques for underwater tuning — use the same methods as those for surface tuning, including those for heavily mineralized areas.

When detecting in a river environment, keep a special eye out for shallow bedrock crevices and "pockets" amongst accumulations of boulders. All sorts of goodies will be deposited in such locations during periods of heavy flooding, just waiting for someone to come along and discover them. In fact, wave your search coil over spots that have been worked *previously* — many a beginning sniper, for example, gets discouraged after a half hour of chiseling impacted rocks out of a crevice, and gives up. Who knows? He may have left behind a large nugget to be found by some lucky prospector the following summer. If you have a good, stable metal detector, if you know how to use it, and if you have the persistence to *keep at it*, maybe that lucky prospector will be you!

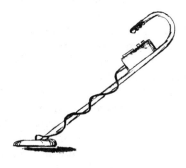

Seven Potential Locations for Profitable Nugget-Shooting

Nugget-shooting No. 1—A very favorable area for the deposition of gold nuggets will be on rocky gravel bars which are underwater at times of flooding. Use a small three- or five-inch search coil to probe around rocks and boulders — the winter floods just might have deposited a pleasant surprise!

Nugget-shooting No. 2—Exposed tree roots near the edge of a stream are always an excellent gold trap. During periods of flooding when the river overflows its banks, roots will act like "tentacles" by trapping gold particles of all sizes. During the California Gold Rush, monstrous nuggets weighing *many pounds* were taken from such locations, and you can be sure the '49ers didn't get all of them.

Nugget-shooting No. 3—Any time you spy an area where bedrock is exposed, make a THOROUGH examination of it. Even if the crevices have already been cleaned out, check it anyway, because not everyone will take the extra time to split open all the tiny "hairline" fissures that extend down into the rock basement. Such a fissure will occasionally widen out into a full-fledged pocket an inch or so below the normal bedrock surface. A small three-inch search coil (shown here) is GREAT for getting into all the little undulations in the bedrock.

Nugget-shooting No. 4—Right now you're looking at a spot which could easily net you many thousands of dollars if you're fortunate enough to stumble onto one which has never been touched (this one *has*). This is a fissure in the bedrock along side of a stream, and even though this particular one happens to be above the water line, you could just as easily find one that is *permanently underwater* and thereby subject to the maximum depositionary action of the river. Any time you spot one of these babies that's filled with tightly packed gravels — above water *or* below — make a thorough investigation with your search coil. You just might be onto a "glory hole" that the old-timers missed.

Nugget-shooting No. 5—The flood current of a river will deposit all sorts of things in amongst piled-up boulders. This nugget-shooter is using the lightweight probe of a "body-mount" detector to check out just such a location.

Nugget-shooting No. 6—Here's the type of spot that every nugget-shooter dreams about — a deep "cleft" in between two boulders in the streamflow. A large nugget that settled here would *stay put* for quite some time, unless a nugget-shooter or pocket-hunter came along and stumbled onto it by chance.

Nugget-shooting No. 7—Any time you find evidence of ancient river gravels perched well above the present streamflow, investigate! This is where the river *used* to flow, tens or possibly even hundreds of thousands of years ago. Try to find an ancient gravel patch that's underlain by bedrock — you may find a gold deposit that's every bit as good as one you'd find by dredging in the present-day river.

CHAPTER FOURTEEN
Gold-Dredging, Prospecting in General, and the Law

Prospectors during the fabulous Gold Rush days really had it made. Thousands upon thousands of square miles of virgin, unpolluted, uncrowded land was at their disposal, available any day, hour, or minute they were overcome by the urge to wander. Aside from previously established mining claims, there was no such thing as "private property." There were no fences, no signs displaying the words "no trespassing," and few peace officers to enforce the meager laws that did exist. The hills and valleys of the great American West were there for *all* men, and so was the plentiful, yellow gold that came with this great land.

Unfortunately, times *do* change, and prospectors today are faced with a number of obstacles their earlier counterparts wouldn't have ever dreamed of. Probably the most striking change is the amount of land that is still open for prospecting, an amount that is shrinking each year. Also a problem is the incredible number of laws and regulations — federal, state, and municipal — that regulate the prospector when he is in the field. But in spite of laws, land closures, etc., the recreational prospector-dredger can still participate in his hobby without doing anything illegal, if he'll just take the time to find out what the laws are.

Before you venture into the field with the intention of mining or prospecting, it is imperative that you first make inquiries to determine the status of the land. Many millions of acres of land in the United States are open to prospecting, dredging, and mineral development — but then again, many millions of acres are not. Generally speaking, vacant, unappropriated lands owned by the *Federal Government* are open for mining activities. When I say "vacant and unappropriated," I mean land that has not been set aside for a specific purpose: Indian reservations and wilderness areas would be examples of this.

The millions of acres of land in the United States that *are* open for prospecting were formerly known as the Public Domain — nowadays the politicians are calling them our "Natural Resource Lands." The Public Domain (to me, that term has more of a meaning behind it) is administered by the Bureau of Land Management, which permits mineral development under the General Mining Laws of 1872. Under these laws, any citizen of the United States (or a person who has declared his intention of becoming a citizen) can go onto the Public Domain and claim in his name deposits of mineral for the purpose of mining.

For every acre of land that is open to prospecting, there is another acre that is closed. Land which is *not* open to prospecting includes privately owned land, National and State Parks, Indian and military reservations, lands belonging to the individual States, city- or county-owned land, reservoirs, permanent lake beds, certain wilderness and primitive areas, State and National Monuments, power withdrawal areas, lands situated below mean high tide, and the beds of navigable rivers. (Few gold-bearing streams of the United States are navigable.)

At this point, you've probably noticed that I've left out one very important classification, and that is the huge acreage of land within the boundaries of our National Forests. Contrary to what you may have read elsewhere, most National Forest land is *open* to prospecting and mineral location. There are hundreds of National Forests in the United States, each of them administered by a "Forest Supervisor." It is the Forest Supervisor who establishes the do's and don't's of mining in his particular Forest, and whatever he says *goes*. National Forest land — as far as prospecting and mining goes — is roughly similar to the Public Domain. There are regions within the Forest boundaries that are vacant and unappropriated, and these areas are open to prospecting. There are also areas which are not open to prospecting, such as acreage set aside for tree plantations, wildlife study, and the like.

Most gold-bearing rivers in the Western mining states flow

through National Forest lands for all or part of their lengths, and it is a wise idea to find out which Forest areas are open and closed. To be safe, communicate with the Forest Supervisor personally. It should be pointed out that prospecting and dredging are not necessarily associated with the filing of mining claims, and areas which are closed to claiming are often open to dredging in the form of recreation. (In fact, just about every Forest Ranger I've ever talked to *regards* dredging as a form of recreation, including those operations which extend over a full mining season.)

Believe it or not, National Forests often have huge acreages of privately owned land within their boundaries. These are parcels of land which were obtained by individuals, businesses, corporations, etc., *before* the surrounding land was incorporated into the National Forest system. The owners of private land in the National Forests are the same as private landowners anywhere — they don't want strangers skulking around in their back yards without darn good cause!

Many miles of choice, gold-bearing rivers — whether they are located in National Forest lands or on the Public Domain — flow through privately owned land. It's a big temptation, I know, to sort of "accidentally" trespass for the purpose of panning, sniping, or even dredging. But just as in Gold Rush days, a person is apt to get his behind filled with buckshot if he goes where he shouldn't! This is especially true in this era of high gold prices, and I've met quite a few landowners who have an "itchy trigger finger" because of it. Any dredger, sniper, or even the casual Sunday afternoon gold panner should conduct a preliminary investigation to determine whether or not a piece of land is available for public use.

There are two principal methods of tracking down the status of a parcel of land. The first is to consult "land status maps" which are published by the Bureau of Land Management, the Forest Service, and occasionally a State's Division of Mines and Geology; these maps are usually issued for areas of key public interest. Land status maps vary from one governmental agency to another in terms of the extent of the area covered, the legend, and the scale. Land status maps are usually printed in several different colors. White, for example, will indicate private land, green a National Forest, and yellow usually signifies the Public Domain. In the Appendix of this book, you will find the names and addresses of where to write various governmental agencies for the purpose of obtaining land status maps.

It must be pointed out that land status maps covering large areas often omit many of the smaller parcels of private land. Private land amounting to a few hundred acres or more is sure to be shown, but not land belonging to the "little guy" which amounts to five or ten acres. This is where the second method of land research comes in, this being the study of *county-owned* land status maps.

Maps which show the location of each and every parcel of private land in a given area are known as "plat maps," and can be found in the Tax Assessor's office of the county in which the land is located. Plat maps are available for public inspection during normal business hours, and all you have to do is *ask*. It does help, however, if you are able to tell the office clerk the township, range, and section in which the land in question is located so that he (*or* she) can select the right map book without having to search blindly. (The township, range, and section system will be discussed in great detail a little later on.)

Once you are looking at the map book, you will notice that the pages are divided by lines into rough squares. These are *sections*, and represent approximately one square mile of land surface. The sections, according to the number of different landowners in each, will be divided further by more lines. Inside the lined areas will be numbers — this is the coding system used by the county to keep track of landowners. Once you've found the piece of land you're interested in, tell the clerk the code number for that parcel. The clerk will then look up the number in the files, and in a couple of minutes you'll have the name and mailing address of the landowner. You can then write (or even visit) that person to secure permission to prospect or dredge on his or her land.

If a given parcel of land is identified by the letters "U.S.A.," this means it is owned by the Federal Government and is part of the Public Domain; unless the land has been withdrawn for a specific purpose, it is open to prospecting. Oftimes, plat maps will identify a parcel of land with the letters "USFS," or sometimes just "FS." When you see this, it means that the parcel is under the jurisdiction of the Forest Service. As in the case of Public Domain land, if it has *not* been appropriated for some specific purpose, it is open to prospecting.

So far the process of checking on a piece of land has been relatively simple, but now I'm going to drop the bombshell. Even though a parcel of land may be publically owned, it may be *closed* to mining activities by the existence of valid, previously established mining claims. A valid claim is one which is kept up to date by the performance of yearly "assessment work," or "proof of annual labor." The certification of yearly labor — *and* a copy of the original claim notice — can be found in the Office of the County Recorder.

There are two types of mining claims — those which are *patented* (these are claims to which an official deed of ownership has been granted), and those which are *non-patented*. The latter type is infinitely more commonplace.

The only rights bestowed to the holder of a non-patented claim are *mineral rights,* and not actual ownership of the property; this type of claim must be renewed yearly by the performance of assessment work. A patented claim *does not* need to be kept up to date by the filing of yearly proof of labor affidavits because it is actually a parcel of private land and is shown on the Assessor's plat maps as such. Trespassing on a patented claim is like trespassing in a man's back yard — it is liable to get you in trouble!

The vast majority of mining claims you'll encounter in the field, as stated previously, will be of the non-patented variety. Since the holder (notice how I don't use the word *owner*) of a non-patented claim owns only mineral rights, he cannot stop you from fishing, camping, hunting, or swimming on his claim, but he *can* stop you from doing so much as placing a gold pan in the water. What you'll have to determine for yourself is, can he *legally* stop you? Many claim holders — particularly "old-timers" in some of the Western mining districts — have a habit of neglecting their yearly assessment work, while maintaining strong feelings of "ownership" over the claim. As a result, claims which appear to be very official from the looks of the field location marker may actually have lapsed back to the Public Domain through default! (This reminds me of one so-called "claim" in Northern California I once investigated. The necessary notices of location were posted in the field, but when I went to the County Recorder's office to trace it, I learned that no such claim existed in the record books. The person who "filed" this claim never recorded it with the county, and was obviously bent on keeping weekenders — who rarely check the records — off the property. Let this be a lesson to you — never believe what you read on a claim marker until you've run it down!)

While you are in an area for the purpose of checking its gold content, it is wise to keep a sharp eye out for claim markers. Usually these are posted on tree trunks, but they can also consist of a sign painted on the face of a large boulder or other semi-permanent object. By law, claim markers must display the name of the claim, the date of filing, and the names and addresses of the persons who are filing. A *smart* prospector always carries a pencil and paper for copying down all pertinent information on any claim markers he comes across, for the purpose of checking them out later at the Recorder's office.

Unlike titled, patented claims which are shown on plat maps, the records of non-patented mining claims reveal themselves only to those who take the time to search through the County record books. This is an art in itself, and unless you've had prior experience in reading official records you may be better off letting the recording clerk help you. Once the clerk has shown you the procedure for tracing, you can generally check on any subsequent claims yourself.

To start the tracing procedure, you will need the information that you copied from the claim marker in the field. The first thing the clerk will ask you is whether the claim is a placer or a lode (hard-rock) location. Placer and lode claims are kept in different sets of books, hence this request. Next, the clerk will ask you the name of the claim and the date it was filed. (The date of filing enables the clerk to select the correct record book from the shelves; the name of the claim speaks for itself.)

Let's create a hypothetical case. The claim you wish to trace was filed on March 15, 1958, and you wish to determine whether or not the required proof of labor has since been filed on a steady, yearly basis. To start off, the clerk will pull the record book which contains the information on claims filed in the year 1958. (Record books are quite large, and often cover up to three or four years of filings under a single cover.) Next, the clerk will find that section of the book with the records for 1958. The year 1958, in turn, is broken down into months, and all claims filed in any given month are listed according to the date of the month they were filed. When the clerk finds the section for March of 1958, he will run his finger down the column until he comes to the 15th day of that month. Scanning this section, now, he finally comes to the name of the claim that you gave him. Now that you know the claim was, indeed, filed with the County Recorder, the next procedure is to check the records for subsequent years to learn whether or not his yearly assessment work was performed. This is where you need to know some of the laws relating to mining.

The period of time for which a proof of labor affidavit is filed is known as an "assessment year." It starts at twelve noon on the 1st day of September following the date of filing, and runs to twelve noon on September 1st of the following year. Our hypothetical mining claim was filed on March 15, 1958. This means that the assessment year for this particular claim started at twelve noon on September 1st, 1958, and ended on September 1, 1959. Any time after September 1st, 1958, the locator of this claim was eligible to file his yearly proof of labor for the assessment year ending September 1st, 1959, but no later than twelve noon on the thirtieth day *after* that date; this is a sort of "grace period" for prospectors who procrastinate! To find out whether or not this was done, consult the list of *filers' names* which is usually found somewhere in the record book. This list, like the section for claim listings, is broken down into years, months and days. Off to one side of the pages will be several columns, with spaces to place check marks after each person's name. In the case of our hypothetical claim, start searching through *each name* in the listing that was entered after September 1, 1958. If you find the filer's name entered *before* the thirtieth day following September 1, 1959, glance to the columns on the side of the page. If there is a check in the column marked "proof of labor" (or sometimes just p.o.l.), the claim holder in question did indeed file the required proof of labor before the end of the assessment year. That person now owns the mineral rights for the assessment year beginning September 1, 1959, and running up to September 1, 1960. Use the same procedures for checking each year from 1960 up to the present. If the claim holder has filed his proof of labor affidavit *on time, each year* with no interruptions, that claim is valid to this very day, and you had better stay off.

Should you really have your heart set on dredging this spot — in spite of the seemingly valid claim — there are a couple of other things you can check on to remove any lingering doubts. One of the provisions of the Mining Laws of 1872 states that a person filing a mining claim must perform "discovery work" within a certain period of time after the filing date. (Each State has its own slight variations of the Mining Laws, and the period of time in question generally ranges from thirty to ninety days.) Within the prescribed time, the locator(s) of a placer claim must excavate an open cut on the surface of the ground and remove not less than seven cubic yards of material. To be sure, there are prospectors who perform discovery work in other ways — such as by dredging — but that's beside the point. What really matters is, was the discovery work *performed.*

When a prospector makes a discovery in the field, he will fill out *two copies* of the appropriate location forms, posting one on the claim and taking the other to the Recorder's office to be filed. On most location forms, there is a blank space for the purpose of describing the discovery work that was made for the benefit of the claim. Most prospectors, rather than wait 'til they've performed their discovery work, will immediately take the partly completed claim form in for filing to secure mineral rights — the prospector then has the State-prescribed time limit in which to perform the discovery work at his leisure. Once the discovery work has been performed, the prospector will take the recorded copy of his location form (which was photocopied and returned to him) and *refile* that same document, this time with all the pertinent discovery information filled in. Sometimes a claim holder will file an entirely new document for the purpose of describing his discovery work, and this is just as legal as the first method. ***

If you want to track down proof of our claim holder's discovery work, start by asking the recording clerk to guide you to the books containing the photostatic copies of claim location forms. (The master record book that contains the names and dates of claim filings will list the specific book and page number of where to find the photostatically copied claim form document.) Once you find the

*** Please see important new information on page 219.   209

photocopied claim form, study it to see if the filer performed any discovery work at the time of location. If he did, the claim is valid, and you can stop checking right there.

If the claim document shows *no evidence* of discovery work at the time of location, go back to the master record book and find the date of original entry (use *this* date because the date on the claim document may be different; it is the *county's* records that count). Next, count off the number of days this particular state allows the prospector to perform his discovery work, and let this be the "expiration date." Now jump back to the name listings in the claim recording book and start searching for an entry by the claim filer *between* the date he originally filed his claim and the expiration date. If there is no entry of a proof of discovery work affidavit (*or* a refiled claim location form) during this "free ride" period, the claim automatically reverted back to the Public Domain on the expiration date. Even though our claim "holder" performed proof of annual labor every year since 1959, his claim is still invalid and is open to refiling!

Let's take a moment to see where we stand. We've checked to see if our hypothetical claim holder has filed his proof of annual labor, and we'll assume he has. We'll also assume he's done the required discovery work within the State-prescribed time limit. It appears beyond a reasonable doubt that our claim holder has done everything according to the books, and has a one hundred per cent, legitimate claim. But wait a minute. There is one more thing you can check on to determine his claim's validity, and that is to check with the county Tax Assessor to learn whether or not he has paid his yearly property tax. (Yes, you read correctly — I *did* say property tax!) Many counties, in many different states, collect a yearly tax on mining property, though in the case of non-patented claims it rarely exceeds ten or fifteen dollars a year. Even so, if the claim holder has failed to pay the required property tax on his ground, he is asking for trouble. If a claim holder goes without paying his property tax, the county Tax Assessor will single out that claim for close scrutiny. If no property tax has been paid for a period of say, two years from the date of the last recorded payment, the Assessor's office will begin collection proceedings. If this doesn't work, the Assessor will remove the claim's file card from the tax roll and officially declare the claim to be null and void, thereby causing it to revert back to the Public Domain.

If you intend to "snatch up" somebody's mining claim by means of the holder's failure to pay his property tax, BEWARE. The failure of a claim holder to pay property tax DOES NOT, at the beginning, nullify the claim; the only thing that would do this is the failure to perform the required proof of annual labor, as per the General Mining Laws of 1872. The only person who can declare a claim to be void because of non-payment of property tax is the county Tax Assessor, and this action may not occur for several years after the tax bill first became delinquent. I must point out that different counties in different states will have their own unique policies for dealing with delinquent taxpayers. If you intend to file on a claim which has property tax outstanding, *check with the county Tax Assessor to make sure the claim has been officially nullified!*

The time will come when you may wish to file mining claims of your own, but like more than one prospector-dredger before you, the many pages of text that make up the Mining Laws of 1872 are apt to seem confusing. To some extent this is true, but once you have studied the Laws for several hours they will begin to make sense. Perhaps the best information ever published on the General Mining Laws of 1872 is contained in a small, inexpensive book published by the California Division of Mines and Geology. It is entitled "Legal Guide for California Prospectors and Miners." Not only does this book explain the provisions of the 1872 Mining Laws in simple, easily digestible language, it also acquaints the reader with the variations of the Laws as they apply in the State of California. Don't, however, let the word "California" mislead you — much of the information is compatible with mining regulations in *other* states as well, making this book one of double value. You can find the address of the California Division of Mines and Geology in the Appendix of this book. ***

In order to file a mining claim, you must first make a bona fide *discovery* — it is not enough to merely guess that a certain mineral is present. To be sure, a lot of guys file a claim after they discover two or three microscopic specks of gold, and while this does constitute a "discovery," it is not the right thing to do. File a mining claim only when there is a *workable, sizable quantity of mineral present*, enough to warrant the investment of time and money for the purpose of developing a *paying mine*. If you file claims just for the purpose of going in and "puddling around" on weekends, you're asking for trouble from the governmental agency that regulates the land. These are the claims the politicians just *love* to invalidate!

But you say you *have* discovered mineral worthy of serious mining activity? OK, here's what must be done. The first step in the location of a mining claim is to post a *notice of location* on the land you are claiming. The notice may be written on a piece of paper, painted on the face of a rock, or even scratched into the trunk of a tree if you can't use the latter methods. In any case, the notice of location *must* contain the following: (1) the date; (2) the name(s) of the locator(s); (3) the name you are giving the claim; (4) the number of acres you are claiming (as in the case of a placer claim, which is the type you will probably be filing), and (5) the distance from the discovery notice to a nearby, permanently fixed object (the junction

*** Please see updated information on pages 235-36. 211

of two streams is a good example of this).

It is a good idea to always carry several claim location forms, which can be purchased at larger stationery stores. These forms contain blank spaces for all the necessary information which must be filled in, with a space set aside for information regarding discovery work when it is finally performed. Fill out *two* of these forms; leave one with the notice of location on the claim, and take the other to the County Recorder's office to be recorded. The copy left on the claim should be placed in a glass jar or tin can to protect it from the elements.

The maximum-sized parcel of land which may be taken for a placer claim by an individual person is twenty acres. If you are working with a partner, the two of you may claim forty acres. An association of *more* than two persons may file a claim as large as 160 acres, with twenty of the total number of acres filed upon going to each individual partner. For example, three persons may file a sixty-acre claim; five persons may file on 100 acres, and eight persons may file on 160 acres, which is the maximum. A claim of this nature is known as an "association claim."

One of the big worries confronting the beginning claim filer is how to lay out and stake the parcel of land he is filing on. Actually, the "staking" part of filing a mining claim is often unnecessary, as in the case of filing on lands which have been taken into the U.S. Public Survey. These are lands which have township, range, and section lines extended over them, breaking the land down into easily identifiable pieces. All you do is identify the parcel of land according to its legal subdivision, write that description on your claim location form, and record the latter with the County Recorder. The boundaries of claims located in this fashion need no staking of any kind, except it is wise to drive a nice, permanent stake at that spot on the claim where the original discovery was made. This is the *discovery stake,* and it is here where you place your notice of location and one copy of your claim location form.

The way the U.S. Public Survey (also known as the "Cadastral Survey") is laid out, lands covered by the Survey are broken down into units called *townships*; the township system is laid out over the land in sort of a "grid" pattern, with hypothetical lines acting as the boundaries. A given township is identified by the way it lies on the grid pattern, which is based upon base lines and meridian lines that are established by the Public Survey. Base lines run *east and west*, meridian lines *north and south*; both are named for a prominent feature of the land such as a city, mountain, etc. Townships which are located *north* of a base line are called "townships north," and the opposite for those south of the base line. When it comes to a meridian line, the terms "range east" and "range west" apply. *Range lines* are vertical lines which run parallel to the meridian, and are spaced six miles apart. *Township lines* run parallel to the base line, and also are spaced six miles apart.

To gain a better understanding of all this, let's study Figure 67. Notice the squares which are laid out to the north of the base line and east of the meridian line. These squares are separated by range lines (running north and south), and township lines (running east and west). Since township and range lines are spaced six miles apart, each square has a total land area of thirty-six square miles. These are the *townships*. Notice how the townships are labeled T1, T2, T3, T4, and T5 going north, and R1, R2, R3, R4, and R5 going east. These abbreviations, "T" for township and "R" for range, are used for easy identification. Let's say we wanted to identify the township that is shaded. This particular township is the *fourth* township north of the base line, and would be known as "township four north." As far as range goes, the township is three range lines *east* of the meridian line, and would be called "range three east." The full description of this township would be "township four north, range three east," to be followed by the initials of the associated base line and meridian. In legal terms, this township would be identified as follows:

T. 4N, R. 3E, etc.

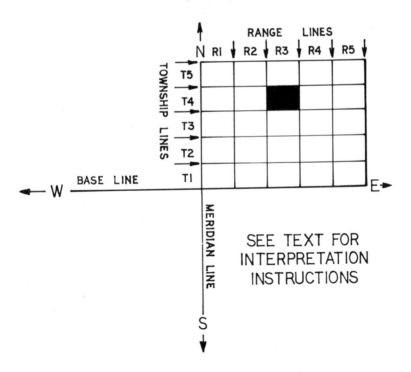

Figure 67—Diagram of township and range "grid pattern."

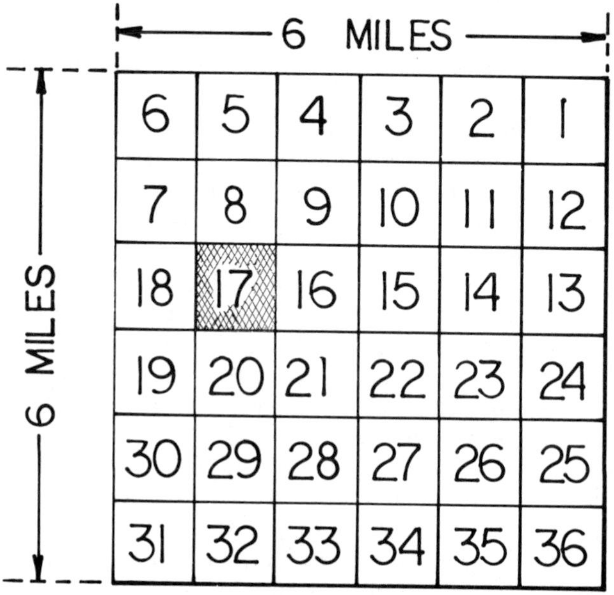

A TYPICAL TOWNSHIP IS SHAPED LIKE A SQUARE, AND CONSISTS OF 36 SMALLER SUBDIVISIONS CALLED **SECTIONS.** THE ENTIRE TOWNSHIP CONSISTS OF 36 SQUARE MILES OF LAND AREA.

Figure 68—Detailed view of a township.

Now let's take a detailed look at a township itself. (Figure 68) Notice how the township is divided into thirty-six small squares. These are *sections,* and each one consists of one square mile. They are numbered one to thirty-six, in the manner shown. If we wanted to identify the *shaded* section and place it in proper sequence with the hypothetical township and range we have just studied, we would write it as follows:

Sec. 17, T. 4N, R. 3E, etc.

It is very important for the *smallest* subdivision of land to be listed *first,* working up to the number of the entire township and range.

Now let's go one step further and look at an exploded view of Section 17. (Figure 69) A section of land is usually divided into four smaller parcels known as *quarter sections*; these are labeled NW¼, NE¼, SW¼, and SE¼. A full section contains 640 acres, and therefore a quarter section contains 160 acres. Quarter sections, in turn, can be broken down into even smaller parcels. Notice how the NW¼ of Section 17 is broken down, into quarters in this case. These are called *quarter sections of quarter sections*, and consist of 40

214

acres each. And now for the subdivision that will be of greatest interest to the claim filer. . . .

Notice how the northwest quarter of the northwest quarter of Section 17 is divided into halves. Since a quarter of a quarter section contains forty acres, a *half* of a quarter of a quarter section consists of *twenty acres*; this is the unit of land measurement used to locate the individually sized, twenty-acre placer mining claim. Referring to Figure 69, let's suppose that a rich section of gold-bearing river ran through the parcel of land that is shaded and you want to file a claim on it. Starting off with the smallest parcel first, this twenty-acre piece of land is the *west* one-half of the *northwest* quarter of the *northwest* quarter, section *seventeen*, township *four* north, range *three* east, and so forth. Let's spell it out legally, now. . . .

W ½ NW ¼ NW ¼ Sec. 17, T. 4N, R. 3E, etc.

This same method is used in figuring the legal subdivisions of parcels located in other portions of a section. A good way to figure out the subdivisions of a *real* piece of land is to purchase a detailed U.S. Geological Survey topographic map and then use a pencil and ruler to divide some of the sections into smaller portions. By practicing in this manner for several hours, you will progress rapidly to the point where you can subdivide a section without even thinking.

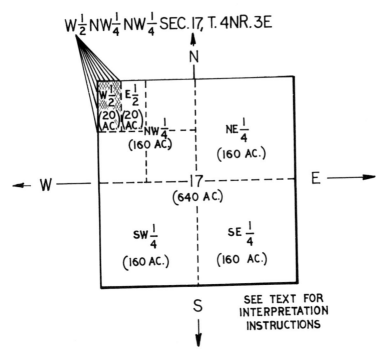

Figure 69—Exploded view of a section, showing key subdivisions.

Once you get this good, you're ready to use your knowledge for the purpose of filing mining claims.

Many millions of acres of land in the Western portion of the United States have not been surveyed, hence there are no township, range and section lines extended over them. When filing a claim in an unsurveyed area, the erection of boundary markers becomes a necessity.

The Mining Laws of 1872 are not specific when it comes to defining the boundaries of a placer claim on unsurveyed land, except that they must be easily traced. It is, however, stated that the boundary lines of the claim *should* run east and west, north and south, so as to conform to Survey lines once they are finally extended over the land. The claim should be in a rectangular, compact form whenever possible. To save you a lot of time in computation, let me say that a parcel of land 1,452 feet long by 600 feet wide equals *exactly* twenty acres. Forget any information you've read elsewhere stating that 1,500 by 600 feet equals twenty acres — it doesn't!

Once you locate a claim on unsurveyed ground, it will be necessary for you to mark the corners of the claim. This is done either of two ways. The *best* way is to drive a 4 x 4-inch wood stake — at least four feet long — into the ground at each corner of your claim. If you don't happen to have wood stakes with you, you can erect a pile of rocks not less than eighteen inches high at each corner. The notice of location is posted on or near the "discovery stake" (or rock pile) which is placed at the point of original discovery. There is no specific law regarding the placement of the discovery stake within the boundaries of a placer claim, but when filing claims on lands which are *unsurveyed*, most prospectors will make the discovery point one "corner" of the claim and arrange the boundary stakes in such a manner as to make it so. Next, the prospector must record the distances from the *discovery* marker to the regular boundary stakes. For example, a prospector might say, "Beginning at the point of discovery, the claim boundary runs 1,452 feet in a westerly direction to boundary stake number one, thence 600 feet in a southerly direction to boundary stake number two, thence 1,452 feet in an easterly direction to boundary stake number three, and finally 600 feet in a northerly direction back to the discovery stake." When you describe a parcel of land in this manner, you are using the "Metes and Bounds" system of land description which actually originated way back in the colonial period of our Nation's history.

It should be emphasized that the posting of boundary stakes and the subsequent definition of their spacing is classed as discovery work, and *does not* have to be performed right at the beginning. As long as the boundaries are posted and defined within the State-prescribed time limit, you are all right.

The locator(s) of any twenty-acre placer claim — on surveyed *or* unsurveyed land — must excavate a "discovery pit," removing not less than seven cubic yards of material. It is tempting, I know, to dig (or in the case of underwater prospectors, *dredge*) several small holes and add up the total yardage removed, but this is not legal. To save you time in computation, an excavation *eight* feet long by *five* feet wide by *five* feet deep will yield just over seven cubic yards of material.

The locator(s) of any placer claim over twenty acres in size must perform one dollar's worth of work for each acre in the claim. This labor must be in the form of actual mining and development work, and not in the construction of tool sheds, cabins, or other surface structures. (Incidentally, officials who manage the Public Lands don't look favorably on claim holders who construct buildings of *any* kind on their claims — too many miners abuse the Mining Laws by constructing recreational cabins, etc., on their claims, and as a result even the most legitimate mining-related structures are coming under scrutiny.)

The yearly assessment work (or proof of annual labor, whichever you prefer) which must be performed on all non-patented mining claims consists of labor and/or improvements which are worth at least one hundred dollars. Assessment work may be performed on or off the claim, on the surface, under the surface, or in the case of dredging claims, *underwater.* What's important is whether or not the labor or improvements so performed actually benefit the claim, and are worth the one-hundred-dollar minimum expenditure.

Most of the laws regulating gold-dredging per se are either municipal or environmental in nature. An example of a municipal law would be one that forbids gold-dredging within the city limits of a community for reasons of "noise pollution." This is fairly reasonable, because anyone who's ever listened to the droning of a dredge engine for hour after hour can realize how it might disturb those who are not afflicted with gold fever. In fact, more than one famous mining town in the far West which owes its *very existence* to gold won't allow dredging within the municipal boundaries, for this very reason. Before you start dredging near any center of population, check with the local authorities to make certain you are not violating city ordinances.

It is *extremely* important that every dredge owner equip his engine with a U.S. Forest Service-approved spark arrestor. (The device that comes standardly equipped on the exhaust port of your engine is *not* a spark arrestor — it's a muffler.) While the odds of touching off a fire with a dredge engine are astronomical, land management officials (and particularly Forest Rangers) will jump down your back for running without one. While inside the boundaries of a National Forest — as you probably will be — you are subject to a stiff citation for operating *any* gasoline-powered engine without a spark arrestor. More than one gold-dredger has been "nailed" for violating this law, so play it safe, and don't let it happen to you.

Even if your dredge is equipped with a spark arrestor, there will be certain areas in which you just can't *run* a dredge. Usually these will be National Forest areas that are extremely isolated, with no fire roads over which emergency vehicles can gain access in the event of a disaster. In cases such as this, Forest Rangers don't necessarily have anything against dredgers, but it's the sheer presence of *people* in isolated locations that makes them worry. Dredge engines don't start forest fires but people *do,* and that's why certain areas are closed to dredging. Usually a land closure of this nature will only be for the hot, summer months when the underbrush is literally a "tinder-box."

The laws created as the result of pressure by environmentalists are affecting nearly everything these days, and gold-dredging is no exception. A lot of conservationists argue that gold-dredging pollutes rivers and streams, resulting in a traumatized fish population. I say poppycock! Gold-dredging is actually *beneficial* to the fish population in a river, because the intake of a dredge pulls up nutrients which are present in the gravels and loosens them up so that the fish can feed on them. In fact, more than one fisherman has told me he'd caught the maximum limit while fishing in a pool immediately downstream from an operating gold dredge — the fish were literally having an orgy on all the underwater worms and algae which the dredge had stirred up, and were biting at anything!

Thanks to relentless pressure by key environmental groups, several Western gold streams are closed to dredging for fear of what the tailings will do to fish spawning beds. In actuality, spring floods do a thousand times *more* damage to a river environment than all summertime dredging operations rolled into one, but how can you make the ecology freaks listen? Some time ago, a fear of possible damage to spawning grounds actually prompted one Western mining state — California — to regulate the sport of gold-dredging. All gold-dredgers in California are required to have a "dredging permit," which lists all the do's and don't's for the dredger; these permits are issued by the California Department of Fish and Game. I know a lot of you will be coming to the "Golden State" to try your luck in the Mother Lode country, and you can obtain your dredging permit by mail before you leave home. The address of where to write — together with additional details — can be found in the Appendix.

The majority of the laws that regulate mining, prospecting, claim filing, gold-dredging and related fields are, for the most part, reasonable. Many of these laws were originally created by the miners themselves for the purpose of self-policing, and if given a decent chance, will continue to serve our Nation for years to come. To be sure, there are a lot of *screwball* laws on the books as well, but they, too, must be obeyed. In summing up, one thing should be emphasized . . . it takes only a *small* number of lawbreakers to spoil things for the *vast majority* of law-abiding citizens, so take care when you go out into the field. The rights you save will be your own!

IMPORTANT NEW INFORMATION ON FILING MINING CLAIMS:

As of October 21, 1976, all newly located mining claims must be registered with the U.S. Bureau of Land Management, IN ADDITION to being filed with the appropriate County Recorder. This new Law (Public Law 94-579, Title III, Sec. 314; dated October 21, 1976, 94th Congress) applies to both placer and lode (hardrock) claims, on BLM *and* U.S. Forest Service lands, in all states of the Union in which mineral location is permitted under the General Mining Laws of 1872.

The new Law requires that all newly located mining claims be registered with the BLM within ninety (90) days after being located in the field. Here are some of the other things required by the BLM when you register a newly located mining claim (as taken verbatim from an official BLM flyer) . . .

1. A copy of location as recorded in the local records;
2. A statement providing the legal description indicating Township, Range, Meridian, State, Section, and Quarter Section;
3. A map showing the survey or protraction grids on which is depicted the location of the claim;
4. A $5.00 service fee for each claim;
5. Evidence of assessment work is also required to be filed with BLM (no fee required).

Any reader of "Dredging for Gold . . ." who is even remotely interested in filing mining claims is advised to contact the Bureau of Land Management for the purpose of obtaining more complete information regarding this new Public Law. You can find the addresses of the BLM's various State Land Offices in the Appendix.

CHAPTER FIFTEEN
"The Gold I Find—
What Should I Do with It?"

When all things are said and done, when all gold has been dredged, sniped, panned or electronically detected, after all mining equipment is put away in mothballs for the winter, one question above all will come to mind. That question is, "What do I do with the gold I've found?" It's a question that's asked time and time again, and I'll try to answer it the best I can.

To start off, let me say that every prospector-dredger I've ever met has fallen into one of three categories — I'm sure you will, too. These categories are: (1) Those who sell their gold to pay for their equipment and trip expenses; (2) those who keep and display it, and (3) those who stash it away awaiting a time when they can get top dollar for it. And then again, some prospectors fall into all three categories at once, keeping some gold to display, selling a certain amount of it, and banking the rest.

Except for the most extreme sentimentalists, the word GOLD is synonymous with the word *money*. Though most people go about gold-dredging with a recreational attitude in mind, there are dredgers who go into the field with the hope of making money. Those who find gold in quantities sufficient enough to sell have two principal routes they can follow— depending upon the nature of the gold that has been recovered — when it comes time to cash in their gleaming wares. If, for example, a dredger has recovered a really sizable amount of gold as the result of a full season's work, the finer flake-type gold can be sold to a refinery or other commercial firm for a prompt cash settlement. This will give the dredger "eating money," and allow him to live comfortably while he waits for that very special person who will eventually come along and pay "specimen prices" for his larger nuggets. I'll get to this matter a bit later.

A question that's frequently thrown at me by the beginning gold-dredger is, "What's the Government paying for gold these days?" You can well imagine the look on his or her face when I answer, "Nothing — the Government hasn't purchased any gold from miners since March of 1968." That last statement, as strange as it sounds, is true. Our Government is *out* of the gold business, and considers gold a "savage, barbaric leftover from the dark ages." (As this book is being submitted for publication, however, it appears that Uncle Sam may be going into the *selling* end of the business; as a preliminary move in this direction, the Government "auctioned off" 753,600 ounces of gold on January 6, 1975.)

In general, fine flaky-type gold is most easily sold to a refiner or precious metals firm that requires it for their business. (They personally don't *care* whether gold is coarse or fine, because all they do is melt it down into bullion anyway and re-sell it for a profit.) The price you can expect to obtain from a refiner, etc., will depend upon the prevailing free-market gold price which is fixed in London, England, every banking day. One thing you should realize is this — in most instances, refineries and other major gold buyers have a minimum "refining charge" which is levied against all persons who sell gold to their establishment. The "refining charge" can actually run as high as $500, making it necessary to sell a relatively large quantity of gold in order to come out ahead after a settlement has been made. This is not to say that a refinery won't purchase small quantities of gold, such as amounts commonly found by recreational prospectors; *they will,* but the high refining charge will completely wipe out any profits that you would have otherwise made off the sale of the gold. This is why gold refineries should be considered only by persons who find more than a casual amount; let's use ten ounces as a minimum figure.

In spite of the somewhat "negative" information just presented, let me say that gold refineries *do* have their redeeming points. Unlike the manner in which dear Uncle Sam used to buy gold from miners, refineries *will* purchase the impurities that are found in placer gold; they won't, however, purchase common "base metal" impurities such as copper or lead. Examples of metals that *would* be purchased are silver, platinum, and the more valuable metals of the platinum group family (iridium would be a good example of this). It should be pointed out that in order to purchase the impurities, the refinery will hit you with an *additional* refining charge for these "side" metals, although it is nothing like the initial charge.

Throughout the United States, there are many thousands of firms that deal in "precious metal scrap," as it is called, and this is another possible market for your fine placer gold. These firms operate in much the same manner as the major refineries — they buy industrial scrap in the form of solutions, sludges, sweepings, residues, etc., that contain precious metals such as gold or platinum, and then separate these metals and sell them for a profit. There is no reason why these outfits shouldn't buy placer gold, as it is much easier to process than the materials they usually handle. You should have no trouble whatsoever locating an establishment of this nature; in fact, it you live in or near one of our larger cities, there may actually be several to choose from!

If you are an average recreational dredger who occasionally recovers a few ounces of fine, flake-type gold, you can easily dispose of your wares by breaking the gold down into small fractions of an ounce and putting it into small sample vials and selling it at rock shows, club gatherings, etc. Many dredgers who do this will break their gold down into one pennyweight, half pennyweight, or even quarter pennyweight sizes and put these measured weights in a *water-filled* sample vial, which makes the gold appear much larger than actual size. I have seen many persons selling gold in this fashion at the rock shows, and believe me, the people go hog wild over it! (It has been my experience that people will go *especially* wild around Christmas-time, when they're out looking for unusual gifts.) It is not uncommon to get prices as much as fifty per cent above free-market price, and I've seen guys up in the California Mother Lode communities selling sample vials to the summer tourists at *double* the free-market price! There is only one thing wrong with selling gold in small quantities like this — it takes an awfully long time to sell enough to pay back your equipment and trip expenses. Of course, if you don't particularly need the money that comes from your gold sales, this will not be objectionable.

If you are fortunate enough to find gold in the form of sizable nuggets, whatever you do, *don't* sell them to a gold refinery for free-market price — you can obtain far more than their actual gold value by selling them to "gold connoisseurs" who want them for their private collections. Also, more than one nugget has been sold to the "tourist type" on the spur of the moment, simply because that person had never seen gold before and wanted it for a keepsake. And finally, you'd be surprised at the number of people who require high-quality placer gold for jewelry purposes — persons in the latter category frequently purchase many ounces of gold at a time, so keep an eye out for them!

The prices you can obtain for coarse, heavy pieces of gold depend upon four principal things: *weight, shape, texture,* and *coloration.* The three latter considerations all add up to determine the "character" of a nugget, which principally is what determines its sale price. While weight *is* important in determining the price of a gold specimen, buyers have been known to shell out many times the actual value in gold weight simply because a nugget had fantastic character. Thornton's Rule Number Eight: "A sizable, attractive gold nugget is worth whatever someone is willing to pay for it!" This is known as *specimen value.*

Let me give you an example of specimen value and how it applies to the prices you can ask for your more attractive nuggets. A few years back, famed California gold-dredger Jerry Keene (who heads the mining equipment firm that bears his name) found a fantastically beautiful, 3½-ounce gold-quartz nugget while dredging in California's North Yuba River. Of that weight, only *one ounce* is actually gold, and yet Jerry has turned down offers as high as $1,500 for this nugget. This works out to roughly $429.00 *per ounce* for the total nugget weight of 3½ ounces. The reason? You guessed it, it's specimen value!

All nuggets are not created equal, and some are worth considerably more than others. In general, any gold nugget which has a quartz matrix showing through is worth substantially *more* than a nugget of solid gold of equal weight. The *coloration of the quartz* also affects the price. Nuggets with white quartz are the most common, and while these themselves are worth a considerable sum, it is a nugget with *tinted* quartz which really brings home the bacon. By "tinted," I mean quartz which has a slight coloration owing to traces of iron or titanium mineralization. Perhaps the most valuable gold-quartz nuggets are those with pinkish, or "rose-colored" quartz. A nugget like this will bring top dollar, and if it's large enough, can actually approach prices in the "thousand dollar an ounce" category.

To be perfectly honest, I must say that it often takes a great deal of time to find a buyer who will shell out many hundreds, and often thousands of dollars, for large specimen nuggets. This is why gold-dredgers who recover such specimens will salt them away, awaiting a time when that certain "right buyer" comes along. Since it is obvious that you wouldn't want to sell high-quality specimen nuggets to a gold refiner, just how do you go about finding that right buyer? The answer is, you don't — you let it be known that you *have* specimen gold for sale and interested parties will come to *you.* After all, if nobody knows you have it, nobody is going to ask what you're selling it for!

The gold that is easiest to sell is *not* extremely coarse gold, nor fine flaky gold — it's small nuggets which weigh anywhere from two or three pennyweights up to about half an ounce. This type of gold is prized by makers of gold nugget jewelry, and is appropriately known as "jewelry gold." If you have gold of this nature, don't let it go for less than twice the prevailing free-market price — *minimum*.

Character is extremely important when dealing in jewelry gold. Most persons who manufacture gold nugget jewelry have an eye out for long, coarse-textured specimens with a deep, rich, brassy coloration. Such nuggets make fantastic necklaces and earrings, and an unusually attractive specimen can net you a handsome sum indeed.

More than one gold-dredger has uncovered bedrock crevices literally filled with jewelry gold, and if you're lucky enough to discover such a treasure-trove, there is a good chance of selling the entire "take" to a jeweler who uses gold nuggets in his work. However, by selling any gold in large quantities, you'll generally get slightly less per ounce simply because the buyer will expect a "quantity discount."

In the past few years, the introduction of the lost-wax casting kit has opened up the world of jewelry making to the average person, and many gold-dredgers now make *their own* nugget jewelry. The finer flake-type gold can be melted to cast the ring, bracelet, etc., while the larger "jewelry" pieces are placed in the setting. By making and selling your own gold nugget jewelry, you can dramatically increase your profits — you can get a nice markup on the fine gold that went into the casting, and a *fantastic* markup on any nuggets used. Don't overlook the hobby of jewelry making. For many, it has turned into a full-time business that brings in far more money than the weekly pay check!

Believe it or not, there are many prospectors who won't part with their gold at *any* price, but choose, rather, to display it. Believe me, there is nothing on earth more gratifying than having a nice collection of gold specimens, pieces of precious metal that you won from Mother Nature through the fruits of your labor. A gold collection will take on *extra* meaning once you prospect and dredge in new and more challenging areas; in time, each nugget in your collection will bring back memories of "the hunt," together with the trials and tribulations that led up to the find. Such a collection will only increase in value, memory-wise *and* money-wise.

I've been fortunate enough to view many a gold collection, and the ones that really stood out in my mind, anyway, were those which were attractively laid out and displayed. A good gold collection doesn't have to consist of monstrous nuggets — just a neat, orderly presentation of the gold you do have.

If you display your gold, I suggest you either purchase — or build — some type of tray or case in which to place your finds. As far as selecting a lining for the case, I've found that gold specimens look their best when laid on top of a piece of dark-colored felt, preferably black or green. The dark felt provides a dramatic "contrast" between the brilliant, yellow color of the gold and the background, and almost makes the gold jump out of the case and right at the viewer.

When displaying specimens that are really worthy of the name "nugget," identify each piece with a neat, concise label. State the weight of each piece, where it was found (unless it's a deep dark secret), and any unusual characteristics of the specimen. If you're planning on displaying your collection in rock and gem shows, you may wish to invest in engraved name plates for your specimens. These really give a collection that "prize-winning look."

If there's one thing in particular that spoils the appearance of a gold collection, it's the presentation of gold that's still contaminated with black sand; this is particularly true when smaller, flake-type gold is displayed in water-filled sample vials. The water in the vial *does* magnify the gold, it's true, but it also magnifies the black sand! Make every effort to remove all foreign substances from your gold before placing it in your collection.

In the past few years, the world has seen a dramatic rise in the free-market price of gold, and it would be a downright lie to say that high gold prices haven't created a boom similar to that of the great Gold Rush of the past century. The technology of *mining* gold has changed, to be sure, but once you get down to basics you'll find that the lust for sudden riches is still there. There is nothing wrong with trying to get rich and raise one's self above the position he presently occupies, except that a person should not place all his faith in the price of gold. You probably get what I'm trying to say, but in case you don't, here it is in simple language — "The free-market gold price is raised and lowered *at will* by fabulously wealthy European individuals who 'speculate' in the most sought-after substance on earth." The price of gold can be at an all-time high one month, but the following month it may be scraping the gutter. If you'd like to know how this is possible . . . well, read on!

Let's suppose that you own gold, a *lot* of gold — ten million dollars worth will do to illustrate the point. On a regular basis, you've been selling certain quantities of your gold to industrial users who require it for goods they manufacture. But let's suppose that one day you get tired of selling your gold at the same "old" price that's been around for several months or so, and you wish to *increase* the price you can get for your gold. Here's how you'd do it. You would collaborate with your wealthy friends and business associates who *also* sell gold to industry, and make an agreement by which all of you would stop selling your gold. Once you and your associates stop selling gold, your industrial customers won't be able to get the substance *anywhere*, and all of a sudden — sometimes in a matter of several days — gold becomes practically non-existent. When gold becomes hard to find, the price naturally goes up. The basic laws of supply and demand apply here perfectly.

Getting back to matters at hand, several months have passed, and you and your associates have succeeded in driving the free-market gold price to astronomical levels. When you think you've played "king of the mountain" long enough, you once again will start selling gold — only this time at an extremely high price. In the international gold market, this is known as *profit taking*, and once gold is again made available, buyers who have long been unable to get the precious metal will step forward and purchase anything they can get. For several days after gold again becomes available, buying and selling will be furious; soon, however, the laws of supply and demand will again take over. Now that the yellow metal is plentiful, the free-market gold price will drop drastically, and the entire cycle of *increase, peaking,* and *decrease* will start all over. But if you carefully follow the trends in the free-market gold price (as this author does), you'll notice one thing — each time the price slips from its peaking point, it doesn't go down quite as far as it did at the end of the previous cycle; and each time the price increases, it goes *higher* than it did the previous cycle. It is in this manner that the free-market gold price is constantly increasing.

Even though the free-market gold price fluctuates greatly, the prices of high-quality gold specimens do not change radically. A one-pound nugget, for example, will fetch five hundred dollars an ounce *(minimum)* regardless of whether the current free-market price is one hundred fifty dollars an ounce or *two hundred* fifty. The reason for this is simple. While the free-market price of gold is changed at will, the availability of raw, placer gold from Mother Nature's storehouse cannot be influenced. As a result, even though the price of gold may be at its ebb, prospectors still get premium prices for their larger specimens with a minimum of "haggling." The price of fine flake-type gold tends to run hand in hand with the prevailing free-market price, especially if you're selling it to a refinery or a dealer in precious metal scrap. To get premium prices for fine gold, you must sell it to individuals in the form of sample vials, etc.

In the past few years, there has been much talk concerning the demonitization of gold. Technically, this Nation has been off the gold standard ever since the year 1934, and no one can deny that our economy has been "going to the dogs" ever since. But now there is a ray of hope. On August 14, 1974, U.S. President Gerald R. Ford signed a Bill permitting American citizens to legally own gold bullion for the first time since 1934. This Bill went into effect at one minute after twelve midnight on December 31, 1974, and while it does not reaffirm gold as the basis of our monetary system, it *does* give Americans the chance to protect themselves against fluctuations in the value of the dollar.

Lord only knows how long we, the American people, will be permitted unlimited ownership of the "stuff that dreams are made of." But whatever role the politicians choose for gold in the future, the person who prospects, dredges, snipes, pans, runs a metal detector, etc., has no worries whatsoever, because gold will always remain a cherished and valuable substance in all parts of the world. You simply can't change thousands of years of tradition by the mere stroke of a pen across a piece of paper — the people of the world will not stand for it.

I cannot dictate what you should or shouldn't do with the gold you find, but I hope you'll take into consideration all the information I've presented in these past few pages. It is truly difficult — especially in these economic times — trying to decide whether to keep your gold or sell it, and therefore I advise you to consider the following fact: The sale of *hard* gold yields *soft* paper money, and while paper may be "*the* thing" as far as putting groceries on your table, when times are bad — *really* bad — it is gold that will reign supreme. This is the way it has been for centuries, and this is the way it shall *always* be.

APPENDIX

CHAPTER FIVE INFORMATION:

Topographic maps, published by the U.S. Geological Survey, have been widely used by prospectors, treasure-hunters, etc., for many years now. Because of their popularity, they can be purchased in map stores, larger sporting goods stores, and perhaps your local prospecting shop. But if you can't find a local source for topographic maps, there are two U.S. Geological Survey offices from which you can order maps by mail. One office is in Denver, Colorado, and distributes maps for those states WEST of the Mississippi River, including Alaska and Hawaii. The other office is located in Arlington, Virginia, and distributes maps for states EAST of the Mississippi. The addresses of these offices are as follows. . . .

Branch of Distribution, U.S. Geological Survey
Federal Center
Denver, Colorado 80225

Branch of Distribution, U.S. Geological Survey
1200 South Eads Street
Arlington, Virginia 22202

Before you can order the correct map(s), you will need an INDEX MAP of the state you're interested in. An Index Map is a large, blown-up map of an entire state, with the boundaries of the individual topographic maps extended over it. Topographic maps are frequently called "quadrangles," and each quadrangle is identified by the name of some prominent feature of the land. You can obtain Index Maps for the states in which you are interested from the offices listed previously. There is no charge for Index Maps, but the price for normal topographic quadrangle maps — at the time of this updating in March 1979 — is $1.25.

* * *

There is nothing worse than going into a new mining district and knowing absolutely *nothing* about the area mineral-wise. Oh, sure, anyone can see that there are creeks and rivers to be prospected, but which ones, specifically, yielded the most gold back in the 1800's? This is where you need detailed geologic information, which is best supplied by the "Division of Mines and Geology" of the specific state in which you're prospecting. To help you obtain this vital information, I will list the names and addresses of where to write for mining literature for each of our thirteen Western mining states. . . .***

Alaska Division of Geological Survey
3001 Porcupine Drive
Anchorage, Alaska 99504

Arizona Bureau of Geology and Mineral Technology
845 N. Park Avenue
Tucson, Arizona 85719

California Division of Mines and Geology
P.O. Box 2980
Sacramento, California 95812

Colorado Geological Survey
1313 Sherman Street, Room 715
Denver, Colorado 80203

Idaho Bureau of Mines and Geology
University of Idaho
Moscow, Idaho 83843

Montana Bureau of Mines and Geology
College of Mineral Science and Technology
Butte, Montana 59701

Nevada Bureau of Mines and Geology
University of Nevada
Reno, Nevada 89557

New Mexico Bureau of Mines and Mineral Resources
Campus Station
Socorro, New Mexico 87801

Oregon Department of Geology and Mineral Industries
1069 State Office Building
Portland, Oregon 97201

South Dakota Geological Survey
Science Center
University of South Dakota
Vermillion, South Dakota 57069

Utah Geological and Mineral Survey
606 Black Hawk Way
Salt Lake City, Utah 84108

230   *** Please see new EASTERN STATES information beginning on page 239.

Washington Division of Geology and Earth Resources
P.O. Box 168
Olympia, Washington 98504

Geological Survey of Wyoming
P.O. Box 3008, University Station
Laramie, Wyoming 82071

CHAPTER FOURTEEN INFORMATION:

It is always a good idea to learn whether or not the area you intend to prospect is *open* for prospecting, and a basic, preliminary method of learning the various open and closed areas involves the study of land status maps.

To start off, it will be necessary to obtain a good map of the state in which you are interested. If the map is of any mentionable quality, it will show the boundaries of any National Forests inside that state, together with their names. If your "target area" is *within* the boundaries of a National Forest, you will need a U.S. Forest Service land status map. If your potential "hot spot" is *outside* of a National Forest boundary, you'll need a Bureau of Land Management land status map. Let's start with the addresses of where to write for Forest Service land status maps.

Our thirteen Western mining states — Alaska, Arizona, California, Colorado, Idaho, Montana, Nevada, New Mexico, Oregon, South Dakota, Utah, Washington and Wyoming — are divided into seven "regions" of the National Forest System. Each region maintains an office in a major city, which serves as sort of an "ultimate headquarters" for all National Forests lying within the boundaries of that particular region. The names of the seven Western Forest Service regions — and their office addresses — are as follows. . . .***

CALIFORNIA REGION:

630 Sansome Street
San Francisco, California 94111

PACIFIC NORTHWEST REGION:

319 S.W. Pine Street
P.O. Box 3623
Portland, Oregon 97208

*** Please see new EASTERN STATES information beginning on page 239.   231

ROCKY MOUNTAIN REGION:

11177 W. 8th Avenue
Lakewood, Colorado 80225

NORTHERN REGION:

Federal Building
Missoula, Montana 59807

INTERMOUNTAIN REGION:

324-25th Street
Ogden, Utah 84401

SOUTHWESTERN REGION:

517 Gold Avenue S.W.
Albuquerque, New Mexico 87102

ALASKA REGION:

Federal Office Building
P.O. Box 1628
Juneau, Alaska 99802

Now that you know the addresses of the Forest Service's seven Western regional offices, it might be helpful if I tell you *which states* lie within the boundaries of each region; this is the only way you will be able to direct your inquiries to the correct regional office, as several states lie within the boundaries of *two* regions.

ALASKA — This far northern state lies entirely within the boundaries of the Alaska Region. ARIZONA — This state lies entirely within the boundaries of the Southwestern Region. CALIFORNIA — The West's greatest mining state, except for a portion located southeast of Lake Tahoe and two *very small* portions straddling the Oregon and northern Nevada borders, lies within the boundaries of the California Region. The portion along the Oregon border lies on the western half of California's northernmost boundary, and the portion on the northern Nevada border is situated in the vicinity of Reno, Nevada. COLORADO — This state, except for a very small portion just south of the east-central Utah border, lies in the Rocky Mountain Region. IDAHO — The southern portion of this state lies within the boundaries of the Intermountain Region; the northern half of the state falls in the Northern Region. MONTANA — This famous mining state is situated entirely within the boundaries of the Northern Region. NEVADA — The state of Nevada, except for a very tiny portion north of the California town of Bishop, is located in the Intermountain Region. NEW MEXICO — This state lies entirely within the boundaries of the Southwestern Region. OREGON — The lush, beautifully green state of Oregon lies entirely within the boundaries of the Pacific Northwest Region. SOUTH DAKOTA — The state of South Dakota, except for the northwestern corner, is situated within the boundaries of the Rocky Mountain Region; the northwestern corner lies in the Northern Region. UTAH — Utah lies entirely within the boundaries of the Intermountain Region. WASHINGTON — The westernmost portion of this state lies within the Pacific Northwest Region, while the remainder lies within the boundaries of the Northern Region. WYOMING — The state of Wyoming is divided into *three* regional areas. The eastern three-fourths of the state is in the Rocky Mountain Region, the westernmost fourth is in the Intermountain Region, and the extreme northwest corner (which, incidentally, includes Yellowstone National Park) lies within the jurisdiction of the Northern Regional office.

When writing any of the Forest Service's regional offices for the purpose of obtaining land status maps, make sure you tell them which National Forest you're referring to, the state in which it is located, and *which portion* of that particular National Forest it is that you're interested in. Also, make sure you specify the type of map that shows private and public National Forest areas in *different colors.* In case the main regional office can't send you the map(s) you specify, they will forward your letter to the Headquarters office of the National Forest in question, which most certainly *can.* U.S. Forest Service land status maps always used to be distributed free of charge, but at the time of this revision (March 1979), they are priced at fifty cents each.

*   *   *

The system by which the Bureau of Land Management organizes its land offices is a bit simpler than the Forest Service method, and more or less follows a state-by-state pattern. Here are the addresses of the BLM's State Land Offices for the thirteen Western mining states. . . . ***

ALASKA LAND OFFICES:

701 "C" Street
Box 13
Anchorage, Alaska 99513

N. Post of Fort Wainwright
P.O. Box 1150
Fairbanks, Alaska 99707

*** Please see new EASTERN STATES information beginning on page 239.

ARIZONA LAND OFFICES:

2400 Valley Bank Center
Phoenix, Arizona 85073

Yuma District Office*
2450 Fourth Avenue
Yuma, Arizona 85364

* The BLM's Yuma District Office has jurisdiction over lands along the Colorado River on *both* the Arizona and California sides.

CALIFORNIA LAND OFFICE:

Federal Office Building, Room E-2841
2800 Cottage Way
Sacramento, California 95825

COLORADO LAND OFFICE:

Colorado State Bank Building, Room 700
1600 Broadway
Denver, Colorado 80202

IDAHO LAND OFFICE:

Federal Building, Room 398
550 West Fort Street
P.O. Box 042
Boise, Idaho 83724

MONTANA LAND OFFICE:*

Granite Tower
P.O. Box 30157
Billings, Montana 59107

* The BLM's Montana Land Office also has jurisdiction over lands in the state of South Dakota.

NEVADA LAND OFFICE:

Federal Building, Room 3008
300 Booth Street
Reno, Nevada 89509

NEW MEXICO LAND OFFICE:

U.S. Post Office & Federal Building
South Federal Place
P.O. Box 1449
Santa Fe, New Mexico 87501

OREGON LAND OFFICE:*

729 N.E. Oregon Street
P.O. Box 2965
Portland, Oregon 97208

* The BLM's Oregon Land Office also has jurisdiction over lands in the state of Washington.

UTAH LAND OFFICE:

University Club Building
136 East South Temple
Salt Lake City, Utah 84111

WYOMING LAND OFFICE:

Joseph C. O'Mahoney Federal Center
2120 Capitol Avenue
P.O. Box 1828
Cheyenne, Wyoming 82001

When writing the various State Land Offices of the Bureau of Land Management, make sure you specify the *specific areas* of the state(s) in question for which you wish to obtain land status maps. As is the case with the Forest Service, the BLM may have to relay your request to a local, regional office, and in most cases there will be a small charge for the map(s) you need.

*   *   *

The California Division of Mines and Geology publishes an excellent book on the subject of mining law that is entitled "Legal Guide for California Prospectors and Miners." While the book is written with California mining law variations in mind, enough of the information is compatible with the laws of other states so as to make it an invaluable guide for *any* prospector. At the time of this update

(March 1979), this author communicated with the California Division of Mines and Geology and was informed that the Legal Guide is out of print. I asked the Division when it would be coming back *into* print, and they said "they were not sure."

Now, I still think the Legal Guide for California Prospectors and Miners is (or *was*) one of the most useful publications ever offered. It will definitely be in your best interest to check with the Division every now and then to see if the Legal Guide has returned to print. Here is the Division's address. . . .

558-4107 S.A
213- 620 - 3560 LA

California Division of Mines and Geology
P.O. Box 2980
Sacramento, California 95812

*   *   *

Any person wishing to dredge for gold in the State of California must have a "dredging permit" which is issued by the California Department of Fish and Game. There are no legal hassles involved in getting a dredging permit, and anybody can obtain one. As of January 1, 1976, California dredging permits cost $5.00

A California dredging permit is issued for a period of one calendar year, and in most cases is valid in all parts of the Golden State (I'll get to the exception in a bit). The permit comes with a list which describes specific streams in which dredging is limited to certain times of the year. For example, if a stream is classed as being "Zone C," it is open to dredging from June 1st to October 15th. Many California rivers are classed as "Zone E," and are open to dredging the year 'round.

There are two types of California dredging permits, *standard* and *special*. A standard permit is issued for dredges with an intake of twelve inches or less, while a special permit is required when using a rig with an intake larger than twelve inches (I doubt if very many of you will be doing *that*). A special permit is also needed if you intend to run *any* dredge in a river that is normally closed to dredging, such as a "Zone C" area during the spring, fall, or winter months. Special permits are valid *only* in the specific areas which are written on the permit, and do not come with the standard list of "open and closed waters."

To obtain a California dredging permit, write to the following address and ask for *two blank application forms* for a Fish and Game dredging permit. . . .

Long Beach   (8)   213- 570 - 5134

California Department of Fish and Game
1416 Ninth Street
Sacramento, California 95814

916-

When you receive your application forms, fill out the necessary blanks on *both copies*, so that the two are identical; these must now be mailed back to the Department of Fish and Game for validation. One of the copies will be kept by the Department, and the other copy will be mailed back to you together with the list of open and closed waters (if applying for a standard permit). If you *are* requesting a standard permit, mail your completed application forms to the Department's Sacramento address. If you are applying for a *special permit*, you must mail your forms to the Fish and Game regional office which administers the waters in which you'll be dredging. You'll find the addresses of the various regional offices on the back of your application forms.

There is one little idiosyncrasy about dredging permits that I should point out. The Department of Fish and Game occasionally forgets to mail back the list of open and closed waters which is intended for use with a standard permit. If you should receive your standard permit, *minus* the list of open and closed waters, write the Department and have them mail you one. In order for a standard permit to be valid, the list of open and closed waters *must* be attached.

CHAPTER FIFTEEN INFORMATION:

If you choose to sell the gold you have found, there are many possible buyers scattered through all parts of the United States. As I mentioned in Chapter Fifteen, you *definitely* should hold onto your larger gold specimens awaiting a time when that "right buyer" comes along, but as far as fine flake-type gold goes, you can either sell it to a refinery (if you've got a large enough quantity to justify paying the high refining charge), or you can contact a firm that deals in precious metal scrap; either type of firm is recommended if you are in need of a speedy cash settlement. If you have only a *very small* quantity of fine gold, you'd be better off putting it into small sample vials and selling it as specimens.

If you've decided to go the refinery route, let me make a few suggestions as to how to go about it. To start off, thoroughly separate all traces of black sand from your gold (this is a *must*, because no refinery that I know of will take gold that isn't immediately ready for processing). The next step is optional, but it is something that should be done. Take your clean, "unpolluted" placer gold to an assaying laboratory and have a *spectrographic analysis* performed on it. This will reveal the exact percentage of gold, silver, platinum, as well as all other impurities. Next, have several copies made of the assayer's report and mail a copy to each of the refineries you're considering dealing with. These firms will study your assay report, and will then give you a "quote" for your material; you can generally expect to get a slightly different price quote from each refinery because of the varying rates for refining charges. The price quotes you will receive are *not* based upon the weight of the gold you intend to sell, but rather, on the number of fine (pure) ounces of gold the refinery can expect to recover from the material you send. After you have received all your price quotes and compared them, you can then ship your gold (by certified, insured mail) to the refinery that offered you the best settlement. It must be pointed out that refineries, etc., are responsible for your gold *only after it has arrived at their facility,* and not one minute earlier. If your gold is lost in transit, it is *your* responsibility to trace it down and locate it.

For your convenience, I will list the names and addresses of the three largest gold refineries in the United States. These firms are considered to be the "big three" as far as gold dealers go, but rest assured there are a lot more than the ones listed here. To list the name of every single refiner — as well as the many firms dealing in precious metal scrap — would take up enough space to publish the latest edition of Webster's Unabridged Dictionary. So for now, here are the names of the "big three" . . . plus one.

Engelhard Minerals and Chemical Corporation
430 Mountain Avenue
Murray Hill, New Jersey 07974

ASARCO
(formerly American Smelting and Refining Company)
120 Broadway
New York, New York 10005

Handy and Harman
850 Third Avenue
New York, New York 10022

If you are a recreational prospector who recovers a few ounces of gold on your yearly vacation, etc., you might check out J & J Smelting and Refining Corporation in Hesperia, California. This refinery is known throughout the mining industry for its quick settlements and low minimum refining charges. With J & J, you can sell gold in amounts as small as five ounces and come through very well, even after refining charges have been deducted. Their address is as follows. . . .

J & J Smelting and Refining Corporation
17474 Catalpa, P.O. Box 727
Hesperia, California 92345

THE NEW "GOLD RUSH"
TO THE EASTERN UNITED STATES:

Many people think of gold-dredging as the one prospecting activity that can be enjoyed only in the Western portion of the United States, in the famous gold-bearing districts of California or Alaska. In the past few years, however, there has been a major new gold rush to many of the original "Colonial" placer deposits in the Eastern United States. (Not many people realize it, but the first genuine "gold rush" in the United States was *not* the one in California in 1849. Rather, it occurred in the year 1799 in Cabarrus County, North Carolina!)

Now, I'm the first person to admit that 1799 is a long, long time ago. Is it possible for a person to hit the Eastern goldfields *today* and come up with significant quantities of the yellow metal? The answer is a loud, resounding "Yes!" Not too many months before this was written, this author was shown samples of placer gold that had recently been recovered by a man dredging in North Carolina. Without a doubt, this gold had the most fantastic "character" I have ever seen. It was coarse, it was heavy, it was absolutely fantastic! It was the kind of gold that would make a dredger abandon all of his claims in California and head for the goldfields in the East!

At this point, I don't need a crystal ball to know what you're thinking: "OK, Matt. . . . Where's the action?" After listening to heaven knows how many people rave about the gold diggin's in the East, it appears that most of the "action" is in the States of North Carolina, South Carolina, Georgia, Virginia and Alabama. However, at least eighteen *additional* Eastern states have produced noteworthy quantities of placer gold, making a grand total of twenty-three that I know of. Right now I will list the names and addresses of where to write for mining literature for each of these twenty-three states. . . .

Alabama Geological Survey
University of Alabama
Tuscaloosa, Alabama 35486

Arkansas Geological Commission
Vardelle Parham Geologic Center
Little Rock, Arkansas 77204

Connecticut State Library
Sales and Publications
Hartford, Connecticut 06115

Georgia Department of Natural Resources
Geologic and Water Resources Division
19 Hunter Street S.W.
Atlanta, Georgia 30334

Indiana Geological Survey
Department of Natural Resources
611 N. Walnut Grove
Bloomington, Indiana 47401

Kentucky Geological Survey
University of Kentucky
Breckinridge Hall, Room 311
Lexington, Kentucky 40506

Maine Bureau of Geology
State Geologist
State Office Building
Augusta, Maine 04330

Maryland Geological Survey
Johns Hopkins University
Merryman Hall
Baltimore, Maryland 21218

Michigan Department of Natural Resources
Publications Room
Stevens T. Mason Building
Lansing, Michigan 48909

Minnesota Geological Survey
University of Minnesota
1633 Eustis Street
St. Paul, Minnesota 55108

Missouri Geological Survey
Division of Geology and Land Surveys
P.O. Box 250
Rolla, Missouri 65401

Mississippi Geological, Economic and Topographical Survey
P.O. Box 4915
Jackson, Mississippi 39216

New Hampshire Division of Resources and Economic Development
P.O. Box 856
Concord, New Hampshire 03301

New Jersey Bureau of Geology and Topography
P.O. Box 2809
Trenton, New Jersey 08625

North Carolina Geological Survey Section
Department of Natural Resources and Community Development
P.O. Box 27687
Raleigh, North Carolina 27611

Ohio Division of Geological Survey
Fountain Square, Bldg. 6
Columbus, Ohio 43224

Pennsylvania Geological Survey
Department of Environmental Resources
Harrisburg, Pennsylvania 17120

South Carolina Geological Survey
State Development Board
Harbison Forest Road
Columbia, South Carolina 29210

Tennessee Division of Geology
Department of Conservation
G-5 State Office Building
Nashville, Tennessee 37219

Texas Bureau of Economic Geology
University of Texas
Box X, University Station
Austin, Texas 78712

Vermont Department of Libraries
Geological Publications
Montpelier, Vermont 05602

Virginia Division of Mineral Resources
Box 3667
Charlottesville, Virginia 22903

Wisconsin Geological and Natural History Survey
1815 University Avenue
Madison, Wisconsin 53706

Before you drop everything and head for the Eastern gold-fields, you should be aware of the fact that finding a good gold area on "open," publically owned land might be somewhat more difficult than locating such a spot in the mining states out West. This is true because practically all of the land in the East is privately owned with the exception of acreage within the boundaries of National Forests. (There is very little Public Domain, or "BLM" land in the Eastern United States.) In many cases, you will either have to confine your dredging operations to gold areas inside the National Forests, or negotiate with private landowners for the right to dredge their property. One thing's for sure, however — some of the gold areas in the Eastern United States are so fantastic, it will be worth your while to do a little negotiating!

NATIONAL FOREST LAND STATUS INFORMATION

There are quite a few National Forests located throughout the Eastern half of the United States. If the gold area in which you are interested happens to be located *within* the boundaries of one of these Forests, you will need a U.S. Forest Service land status map to make certain you do not wander onto any parcels of private land which may also be located inside the Forest.

National Forests in thirteen of the states listed earlier are administered by the Eastern Regional Forest Service Office in Milwaukee, Wisconsin. These states are: Maryland, New Jersey, Maine, New Hampshire, Indiana, Pennsylvania, Vermont, Connecticut, Michigan, Minnesota, Missouri, Wisconsin and Ohio. Here is the address from which you can order land status maps for National Forests in these states. . . .

U.S. Forest Service
Eastern Regional Office
633 West Wisconsin Avenue
Milwaukee, Wisconsin 53203

National Forests located in the ten remaining states are administered by the Southern Regional Forest Service Office in Atlanta, Georgia. These states are: Arkansas, Tennessee, Mississippi, Alabama, North Carolina, South Carolina, Georgia, Virginia, Kentucky and Texas. Land status maps for National Forests located in these states may be ordered from . . .

U.S. Forest Service
Southern Regional Office
1720 Peachtree Road N.W.
Atlanta, Georgia 30309

PUBLIC DOMAIN LAND STATUS INFORMATION

As I mentioned earlier, there is very little Public Domain land in the Eastern United States. However, there is always the possibility that a good gold-bearing area just might be located on some tiny parcel of Public Domain land right in the middle of a vast ocean of private property. You will need a Bureau of Land Management land status map to check out any area not inside the boundaries of a National Forest. Here is the address of the BLM office that handles inquiries for all of the Eastern states listed previously . . .

U.S. Bureau of Land Management
Eastern States Office
7981 Eastern Avenue
Silver Springs, Maryland 20910

The very best of luck to all of you gold-dredgers who try your luck in the goldfields of the Eastern United States!

ABOUT THE AUTHOR . . .

Matt Thornton was born in Chicago, Illinois, in 1950, and moved to the "Golden State" with his parents when he was nine. To prospect for gold was a kind of "lifelong dream" of Matt's, even as a young child, and he made up his mind that he would one day "strike it rich" — or at least try. It wasn't until 1969 when he finally started pursuing the hobby of gold prospecting, after contracting a serious case of "gold fever" from the members of a local mining and prospecting club. The guidance and advice imparted to Matt must have fallen on receptive ears, for in less than one year he acquired enough knowledge of gold and gold mining to sell his first writing effort to a national treasure magazine in 1970. (He has since had numerous other articles published in the various "treasure rags.") The following year, in 1971, Matt purchased a suction dredge and, being fortunate enough to "chum around" with a large number of highly experienced dredgers, acquired a better-than-average knowledge of underwater gold mining.

Matt Thornton resides in Hollywood, California, and spends his time working on special writing projects, prospecting for gold and gemstones, and researching new areas for possible future exploration.

```
  ´´
  818              818
  150              150
  275             ─────
 ─────             968
 1243              174
  174            ──────
─────            H̶4̶2̶
 1417
  175               ̶2̶
 ─────           ──────
 1242             1142
                   2̶5̶
  350      J        275
    3      F      ──────
 ─────     M      1417
 1050
           

 250  3
   ─────
     750
     150
    ─────
     900
```